café

2000 Contest Questions
for Parties, Fund-raisers
School Events & Travel

By Howard Rachelson

Vision Books International
2002

ISBN 1-56550-090-3

Library of Congress Card Number 2001135164

Book design by Illumination Graphics
www.illuminationgraphics.com

Vision Books International
Mill Valley, CA 94941
(415) 451-7188
www.vbipublishing.com

Contents

Introduction

In their 1993 national bestseller, The Dictionary of Cultural Literacy, authors Hirsch, Kett, & Trefil defined Cultural Literacy as the core body of information that no literate person should be without; information that our culture considers useful, interesting, and worth preserving. The authors offered readers thousands of essential facts, data, and concepts in dictionary form.

Howard Rachelson has added a competitive element to the notion of Cultural Literacy. Since 1983 he has created a set of 15,000 culturally significant trivia questions in dozens of categories. He has hosted hundreds of live trivia events throughout the San Francisco Bay area including private parties, school events and Quiz Bowls, weekly pub trivia contests, book store contests, and fund-raisers for schools and social organizations. Howard also hosts a Web site, Trivia Café (www.triviacafe.com), featuring Question of the Day, Question of the Week and a weekly contest.

We are information sponges. Most people are intelligent and curious. We read books, newspapers, and magazines, watch television and listen to radio. We surf the Internet and get information as soon as it happens. Sitting in our pajamas, we can check a sports result, a weather forecast, or a breaking news event at the other end of the world, in seconds! We are simultaneously entertained and informed.

We've encountered a great deal of information over the years, but how much of it do we remember? How much can we quickly recall? Frequently names of people and places go in one ear, out the other. There are too many facts to remember everything! We all, however, recall some degree of what we've experienced. Some people, and you are hopefully one of them, take pride in being able to recall the names of people and events that create our world, past and present.

Modern TV quiz shows are more popular than ever. If we consider the decades-long success of television's Jeopardy, Comedy Central's Win Ben Stein's Money, the popular Who Wants to Be a Millionaire?, the combination quiz show and Survivor-clone The Weakest Link, not to mention the irreverent computer game turned TV show You Don't Know Jack, we can see that trivia is hotter than ever. Virtually every day of the week we can turn on the tube and watch someone win, or lose, thousands of dollars in a short half-hour segment. Now Howard suggests that you not just sit like a couch potato and watch these shows. Get involved.

Included in Trivia Café: 2000 Questions for Parties, Fun-raisers, School Events, Travel
1. How to host a trivia contest for a house party or fund-raiser.
2. Question sets for parties and fund-raisers organized in groups of ten.
3. Trivia for Travelers for trivial fun on the road, in the air or at the beach.
4. Question sets for school events.
5. General enlightenment sets by categories.
6. Quiz Master - more difficult question sets for those up to the challenge.

How to Host a Trivia Event
Turn your party into a Trivia Café

You can easily host your own trivia contest at your house party, for your social organization, as a fund-raiser or a school event. It's easy to create an exciting activity to get dozens of spirited people involved interactively, and raise money for an organization at the same time. Minimal preparation is needed to turn your home into a trivia café.

For a new and original party within a party, you can conduct a trivia game at your private house party. Two or three rounds of ten questions will constitute an exciting one-hour contest. In the middle of your party, when all the guests have arrived and sufficiently schmoozed, START THE GAME.

The number of teams depends on the layout of your house. As long as you have at least two teams, you will have a great game. You can plan the composition of the teams in advance or make up teams randomly (using playing cards, for example).

Position the teams casually at tables, on the floor, around the sofa. Party trivia goes perfectly well with food and drink. You can play the game during or after a meal or snacks.

How many people can participate? The more, the merrier, that's how many. The size of the room will help you determine how many people to invite. A trivia contest is be played in teams - the ideal team size is 6 to 8 people, for best team dynamics (laughter, knowledge, and arguments). In case of a fund-raiser held in a large room, the goal is as many people as possible.

Choose one of your friends to be the game host or question master. Select someone to create an enthusiastic and competitive atmosphere. Choose someone who can regulate the pace of the game and read the questions slowly, clearly and deliberately.

LET'S BEGIN A GAME - USE THE QUESTIONS IN THIS BOOK!
First distribute a blank answer sheet and pencil to each team. The host reads the questions, one at a time, and gives the team a short, reasonable time to come up with an answer. Teams discuss and debate without the other teams overhearing. Choose one person on each team as the writer, scribe, or recorder, someone with good handwriting, someone who will make a decision on an answer when the players are deadlocked! The buck stops with the writer!

Ten questions make one round. Two to four rounds make a great game!

At the end of each round, collect the sheets and pass them to the correctors (volunteers). The question master then reads out all the correct answers. As the questions are being answered, correctors mark the team answer sheets according to the scoring system, which follows.

METHOD OF SCORING
1. Every question with a single answer is worth TWO POINTS.

The answers need not coincide exactly with the printed answers in this book. If the spirit of the answer is correct, that's sufficient. If teams made the correct identification, then points should be given. If an answer is close but not exact, award points according to your discretion - one point for partial credit, as long as all correctors do the same.

If the answer is a person's name, the last name is necessary and sufficient for the team to receive two points, (unless the question requires the person's full name). If the correct last name is given with an incorrect first name, the answer is wrong.

2. Questions with multiple parts are worth ONE POINT EACH part.

When there are two or more parts to a question, each individual part is independent and is worth one point. For example, if a question is "Name the three U.S. states whose names begin with the letter C," the answers "California, Colorado, and Connecticut" would be worth one point each.

MARKING THE ANSWER SHEETS
When correcting the answer sheets, the correctors should write a 0, 1, 2, or 3 in the left column of the answer sheet beside each answer. Thus you'll know that each question has been corrected, and double-checking the score sheets will be a simple task. Write the team's score for each round at the top of the page, then keep a cumulative total of all points scored by each team on the Master Score Sheet. (See Appendix II)

WHO WINS THE GAME?
At the end of the game (which can be any number of ten-question rounds), the team with the highest score is the winner, and ideally will receive prizes. The value of the prizes is not as important as the principle: WE WON THE GAME! Simple prizes are appreciated.

You can reward 2nd and 3rd place teams also. Why not a Booby Prize to the team with lowest score? They are truly the weakest link.

WHERE TO GET PRIZES
For a group fund-raiser, you can solicit prizes in advance from local merchants or members of your organization. Prizes such as movie passes, free meals at restaurants, bottles of wine for adult winners, plants (used as centerpieces of each table), T-shirts with Trivia Game Winner emblazoned on them, small tablets of writing paper with Trivial Thinker, will be greatly appreciated.

HOST A FUND-RAISER FOR A SCHOOL, COMMUNITY ORGANIZATION OR CHARITY

Have a group fund-raiser with almost no expense, and make a bundle in a couple of hours!

One chairperson should oversee four important committees:
- Game committee (who find the game host and prepare the questions and blank answer sheets).
- Prizes committee (who gather prizes for team and raffle winners).
- Food committee (who choose a menu and organize volunteers to bring food. A subset of the food committee can be the serving committee).
- Promotions committee (who make and distribute fliers advertising the event not only to members, but to the outside world, trivia buffs and fans of team competition in the general community. Think of the millions of TV quiz show junkies out there. Be sure to include sample questions, and send out press releases to the newspaper for free publicity.

Maximize your income and minimize your expenses by holding your event in a room that costs you no money. If your social group is affiliated with a church, synagogue, or club, you can probably gain access to a large meeting room for minimal or no expense. Alternately, if one of your group members has a large house, you could hold your fund-raiser there.

FREE FOOD

Once you have identified a room at minimal expense, your next goal is to acquire refreshments at no cost. Have volunteers bring self-made food dishes, such as cakes, chips and dips, cheese and crackers, veggies, spaghetti, pizza, etc. A wonderfully satisfactory arrangement would to provide munchies such as pretzels, popcorn, M & Ms on each table. Probably local merchants and restaurants can donate food items in exchange for FREE PUBLICITY.

EAT AND PLAY, PLAY AND EAT?

A trivia contest can be waged before, during, or after a meal One suggestion is that participants eat dinner first, then play trivia during dessert. If all food is snack food or desserts, people can munch between rounds. Often it's good to have a long INTERMISSION for participants to meet and greet and talk about the questions that, like a 25 pound tuna, got away.

HOW MUCH TO CHARGE FOR ADMISSION

That depends on where you live and how much money people are used to paying for social activities. For a full evening fund-raising activity, participants are generally willing to pay $7 to $15 per person (or even more, up to $35 for an elegant affair) for admission, depending on how much food is included, the status of the event, and/or whether meals are included or for sale.

RAISE MORE MONEY WITH A RAFFLE

You can raise a nice bundle of money for your organization with a raffle, either for prizes or for money. Sell tickets for $1, six for $5, or, depending on the quality of the prizes, sell tickets for $5 or more. Arrange a half-and-half raffle, in which the winners receive half the money, and the organization keeps the other half. In this manner, you can make money without being required to put up raffle prizes. Alternatively, your members can solicit raffle prizes from local merchants, and you can keep all the money from the raffle.

If you are organizing a school fund-raiser, charge an entrance fee for parents, and offer free admission for kids. Therefore most parents will attend, since they won't need to keep kids home with a baby sitter. Since the entrance fee is minimal, sell food, such as pizza, hot dogs, potato chips, soft drinks, and desserts.

For a middle school or high school, the students can play and teams will be ideally composed of kids and parents. One of the great aspects of a school trivia night fund-raiser is that parents and students work together and trust each other's instincts in building a competitive team.

If the children are too young to participate (elementary schools), have child-care available.

HOW MUCH WAS MADE? DO THE MATH
If one hundred people attend a fund-raiser, and each person pays $10 to participate, buys $10 in food, and invests $5 for a raffle, you can make $2,500 for your organization in an exciting, fun-filled 3-hour event!

PUBLICITY
Create a simple flier on your computer and make photocopies. Mention the fact that EVERY TABLE IS A TEAM, and no individual is put on the spot. Encourage players to form a team with their most trivial friends or come alone and join a team. Include five or six sample questions! Mention PRIZES TO WINNERS!

Write a short press release with sample questions about your event and mail it to the local newspaper about 3 weeks in advance. You can get a large turnout!

TO SUPPLEMENT THE GAME - A MUSICAL ROUND
If you are highly motivated, create a music trivia round on tape or burn a CD from your computer. Mix up four to six songs, about 30 seconds of each. Here are some sample categories you could include in a MUSIC TRIVIA ROUND.

* **Classical music** - name the composer and the name of the work
* **Show tunes** - name the stage show or movie that included this song
* **Rock and roll** - name the song title and the performer or group
* **Name That Tune** - identify the song title
* Name the **mystery singer** and the song (Stand By Me, sung by Muhammad Ali)
* Identify the **geographical location** in the title (I Left My Heart in San Francisco)
* Find the name of a **person** in the title (A Boy Named Sue)
* Name the **number** in the title (Just the Two of Us)
* Identify the **profession** in the title (If I Were a Carpenter)

Generally choose songs which add to the party spirit. Leave a short space between songs on the tape, or pause the tape player, so the teams will have time to figure out and write down the answers, as in every other round. Pick songs appropriate to the ages and interests of your participants.

A PICTURE IS WORTH A THOUSAND WORDS: ADD A VISUAL ROUND

Good rule of thumb is to use as many visuals as musicals. Cut out photos from newspapers or magazines or download from the Internet. Make photocopies so that the number of pictures available is about half the number of participants (two people can share each photo). Feeling techie? Prepare all photos in your computer and project a slide show to the entire group.

Include photos of famous people, great paintings (name the artist), pictures of world cities, and ask the players to identify them. Photo buff? Shoot a roll of slides of photos from magazines and books and project them on a viewing screen during the game. Create a digital photo shop slide show to project on a screen or wall.

Example of a four-round trivia party format, ideal for fund-raisers or school events.
Round 1: ten spoken questions
Round 2: mini round of five musical and five visual questions
Round 3: ten more spoken questions
Plus a BONUS question - a bit tougher and worth three or more points

Party Rounds

Trivia Café Party Rounds
Party Questions Round 1

1. What type of annoying insect is named for a colorful article of clothing?

Yellow jacket

2. Which human organ secretes bile, forms blood proteins, and stores vitamins for later release into he bloodstream?

Liver

3. What Colorado town with a precious name is home of Coors Beer?

Golden, Colorado

4. What country, part of the British empire, has been called The Jewel in the Crown?

India

5. What two tools used by communist industrial and agricultural workers were displayed on the flag of the Soviet Union?

Hammer and Sickle

6. Tom Hanks won the Academy Award as Best Actor two years in a row, 1993 and 1994, for his roles in what two films?

Philadelphia / Forrest Gump

7. From what modern languages do we get each of these words?
a. Chocolate
b. Opera
c. Dungarees

Spanish
Italian
Hindi (language of India)

8. How does one say: "I Love You" in each of these languages?
a. French
b. German
c. Spanish

Je t'aime
Ich liebe dich
Te amo

9. When this Indonesian volcanic island exploded in August 1883, it blew the island apart and caused a tidal wave that killed more than 36,000 people. What was it?

Krakatoa or Krakatau

10. What innovative, sometimes controversial French sculptor in 1904 unveiled his bronze work of a contemplative male, that he called Le Penseur?

François Auguste René Rodin 1840-1917 (The Thinker)

Party Round 2

1. How many times can someone successfully perform hara-kiri (also known as hari-kari)?

Once. Hara-kiri is a ritual suicide practiced by Japanese samurai

2. The Grand Canyon was carved out of solid rock by the cutting action of what river?

Colorado River

3. What is the fastest growing plant- it can increase up to 35 inches (or 90 cm.) in one day?

Bamboo

4. What 1455 book was the first ever printed using movable, reusable type?

Gutenberg Bible

5. What is the northernmost city ever to host the Olympic Games?

Lilljehammer, Norway, 1994

6. What huge limestone mass lies on the southern coast of Spain?

Gibraltar

7. When her mother, Queen Juliana, abdicated the throne in 1980, her daughter, Beatrix, became Queen of what European country?

Netherlands

8. In the 1200s the Persians introduced what exciting sport played with an animal, today played with a ball?

Polo, played with a goat or small animal used as the live ball and still played in Afghanistan

9. Identify the composers of these musical works from the Baroque era:
a. The Four Seasons
b. Royal Fireworks Music

Antonio Vivaldi
GeorgeHandel

c. The Art of the Fugue

Johann Sebastian Bach

10. If you roll a pair of dice, what is the mathematical probability that the sum of the dice will be an even number greater than 5?

14/36 or 7/18 or 39%

Party Round 3

1. March is the third month of what calendar?

Gregorian, created by Pope Gregory XIII in 1582

2. Let's go to Fifth Avenue in New York City: In what year did the Empire State Building open? (margin of 1 year)

1931 (margin 1 year)

3. Inventor Thomas Edison improved the major infrastructure of New York City in 1881 when he installed the world's first what?

Electric power plant

4. From 1954-1969 he served as the first president of North Vietnam, and he later led North Vietnam's struggle to defeat the U.S. supported government in South Vietnam. Who was he?

Ho Chi Minh

5. The first vaccine, developed by the English physician Edward Jenner in 1796, protected people against what disease?

Smallpox

6. At the end of World War II, the victorious Allies divided Berlin, the German capital city, into what four sectors?

Eastern or Russian / French / British / American

7. Can you name two Shakespeare plays that refer to geographical locations in the title?

The Two Gentlemen of Verona / The Merry Wives of Windsor / The Merchant of Venice

8. This singer and songwriter from New Jersey produced ten consecutive top-ten hits from 1984 through 1987. Who was he?

Bruce Springsteen

9. It is said that when he returned home after serving as Ambassador to France in 1789, he brought the first pasta making machine to America. Who was he?

Thomas Jefferson

10. The Simpsons first appeared in the mid-1980s as a short segment on what woman's Emmy Award winning TV series?

Tracy Ullman

Party Round 4

1. By the year 2000, America's 10 largest hotels were all located in what city?

Las Vegas

2. In 1998, he became the first Hispanic musician inducted into the Rock and Roll Hall of Fame (located in Cleveland, Ohio). Who is he?

Carlos Santana

3. What period of human culture followed the Stone Age and preceded the Iron Age?

Bronze Age

4. The campy, 1970s disco group the Village People had three Top 40 hits. One was YMCA. What were the other two?

In The Navy / Macho Man

5. Identify the film title for these actresses who won Golden Globes for Best Actress in a Musical or Comedy,
a. 1999: Gwyneth Paltrow
b. 1997: Madonna
c. 1991: Julia Roberts

Shakespeare In Love
Evita
Pretty Woman

6. Who was the first British prime minister in the 20th century to serve three consecutive terms?

Margaret Thatcher

7. Give the four-letter words for:
a. A planet with red sand
b. Basketball star Bryant
c. Japanese instrument with 7 or 13 silk strings stretched over an oblong box.

Mars
Kobe
Koto, similar to a zither

8. This plant, native to hot, dry regions of the U.S. and Mexico, is grown for ornament, fiber, and food, but more famously, as the main ingredient of tequila. What is it?

Agave

9. Name the largest city in each of these places:
a. Scotland
b. Israel
c. Alabama

Glascow
Tel Aviv
Birmingham

10. Since 1962 this musical group from New Jersey amassed 48 entries on the Billboard Hot 100. It has been said that they were to the East Coast what the Beach Boys were to the West. What group is this?

The Four Seasons

Party Round 5

1. Fearing that its name might lead to the spiritual pollution of Chinese youth, China banned the sale of which Yves Saint Laurent perfume product in stores across the country?

Opium

2. Which two Roman politicians and generals conspired to assassinate Julius Caesar?

Brutus and Cassius

3. The Manhattan Project was the code name for what effort?

To develop atomic bombs for the U.S. during World War II

4. People who disregard conventional standards of behavior are sometimes called bohemians. The historical region of Bohemia is located in what present day country?

Czech Republic

5. One of Woody Allen's best films is the 1986 movie, "Hannah and Her Sisters." Which three actresses played the roles of Hannah and her sisters?

Mia Farrow
Diane Weist
Barbara Hershey

6. What are the two major divisions of the Islamic religion?

Sunni / Shiite

7. Which of these events occurred FIRST: the computer chip was patented, the Berlin Wall was erected, the birth control pill was approved by the U.S. Food and Drug Administration?

Computer Chip 1959 / Berlin Wall 1961 / Birth Control Pill 1960

8. In which city is each of these universities located?
a. Sorbonne
b. Radcliffe College
c. University of Virginia

Paris
Cambridge, MA
Charlottsville

9. This French artist grew only to a height of 4'6", suffered from a number of physical ailments, and died in 1901 at the age of 36. He is famous for his posters of music halls, cabarets, and circuses. Who was he?

Henri Toulouse-Lautrec

10. The Beatles won the Academy Award only once in their career - Best Original Score for what 1970 film?

Let It Be

Party Round 6

1. Silver is the traditional gift for which numbered wedding anniversary?

25th

2. Which has a higher rank: Duke or Earl?

Duke

3. What was the title of the first album released by The Grateful Dead in 1967?

The Grateful Dead

4. The Scots were a Gaelic tribe that migrated in the 6th century A.D. to the northern part of Britain, from where? Ireland, Belgium, or Holland?

Ireland / the word Scotti is Latin for Irishmen

5. Who is the main female character in Margaret Mitchell's Gone With the Wind?

Scarlett O'Hara

6. This book is considered a milestone in the history of feminism. It is called A Vindication of the Rights of Women, and was written by Mary Wollstonecraft in what year: 1792, 1892, or 1992?

1792

7. Phrases containing the word Saint:
a. A volcano of Washington state
b. The capital city of Newfoundland
c. One of the 12 Apostles, who doubted that Jesus had risen from the dead until he saw the wounds

Mount Saint Helen
St. John's
St. Thomas, Doubting Thomas

8. Which Italian violin maker developed the proportions of the modern violin and created some of the finest instruments of all time?

Antonio Stradivari, also called Antonius Stradivarius (1644-1737)

9. Marilyn Monroe died in 1962 at what age? How?

Age 36 / Drug Overdose; originally Norma Jean Baker (1926-1962)

10. How are Israeli postage stamps physically different from those of all other countries? (no relation to currency values...)

The glue is kosher

Party Round 7

1. What two oceans meet at the Cape of Good Hope?

Atlantic and Indian Oceans meet at the southern tip of South Africa

2. What was the first company to use a moving assembly line to create its large complex product?

Ford Motor Company

3. This British soldier, adventurer, and writer led a rebellion of Arabs against the Ottoman Turks in World War I. Who was he and which actor played him on film?

Lawrence of Arabia/ T.E. Lawrence / Peter O'Toole

4. In what year and location did Martin Luther King, Jr. deliver his speech: I Have a Dream?

1963 / Lincoln Memorial / On The Mall in Washington, D.C.

5. Born in 1937 in the Bronx, he grew up to release 18 comedy albums, win three Grammy Awards, star in 10 solo HBO comedy specials, ten movies, and guest star 130 times on the Johnny Carson Tonight Show. Who is he?

George Carlin

6. What are these words that sound like terms from baseball:
a. Author of the Iliad and the Odyssey?
b. A hard, crystalline, colorless form of carbon?
c. A type of canoe?

Homer
Diamond
Dugout

7. What is the only mammal that can fly?

The Bat

8. Former President Johnson, his wife and two daughters all had the initials L.B.J., which abbreviated what?

Lyndon Baines / Lady Bird / Lucy Baines / Linda Bird

9. In 1582 Pope Gregory XIII sponsored a new solar calendar to replace an older calendar in effect since 46 B.C., that had been introduced by what person?

Julius Caesar - Julian calendar

10a. In 1602, explorer Bartholomew Gosnold became the first European to set foot in what region of the new world along the Atlantic Ocean that he named after his home country?
b. Living there with his wife and family, he named an island after his eldest child. What was it?

New England

Martha's Vineyard

Party Round 8

1. In many religions, including Christian, what is the name of the spirit of evil, ruler of hell, and foe of God?

The Devil or Satan

2. Give the associated words or phrases beginning with "go":
a. A novel by Mario Puzo
b. Do unto others as you would have others do unto you.
c. Former Portuguese colony of southwest India

Godfather
Golden Rule
Goa

3. The largest lake in Africa (third largest in the world) is named after a famous queen. What is this lake?

Lake Victoria

4. Developed in the 1930s, anabolic steroids were used to restore body weight in concentration camp survivors, as treatment of anemia and breast cancer. Since the 1950s they have also been used and abused by athletes seeking to enhance performance. Anabolic steroids are derived from what naturally occurring product?

Testosterone

5. Name these Julia Roberts films:
a. In 1999 she played an American movie star who fell in love with a London book store owner played by Hugh Grant.
b. In 1993 she starred with Denzel Washington in a film based on a John Grisham novel.
c. In 1995 she played a maid who worked for the infamous Dr. Jekyll, played by John Malkovich.

Notting Hill

The Pelican Brief

Mary Reilly

6. Which crew member of Apollo 11, an astronaut with a nickname, was the second human being to walk on the moon (July 20, 1969)?

Edwin "Buzz" Aldrin

7. If a cone has a circular base of diameter 10 cm. and a slant height of 10 cm., what is the volume?

226.725 cubic centimeter, and the formula is 1/3 (area of base)*(height)

8. What two countries beginning with the letter B share a land border with Yugoslavia?

Bosnia / Bulgaria

9. How many gods are there in Buddhism?

None

10. The name of what disease means, in Italian, bad air?

Malaria - Italian, from mala aria, bad air

Party Round 9

1. One of the earliest fossilized remains of modern man was discovered in North China and is estimated to be 500,000 years old. What is it called?

Peking Man

2. Which U.S. state capital city was named after a knighted British navigator and writer?

Raleigh, North Carolina, after Sir Walter Raleigh

3. Which day of the week is named for the Scandinavian god of wisdom, poetry, farming, and war?

Wednesday, named for Odin, sometimes called Woden

4. Who directed the 2000 film Crouching Tiger, Hidden Dragon?

Ang Lee

5. Which person was the U.S. ambassador to the United Nations from 1971 to 1973, then later became President of the United States?

George H. Bush

6. Which river rises in the mountains of West Virginia and flows eastward along the Virginia-Maryland border into Chesapeake Bay?

Potomac River, which flows through Washington, D.C.

7. According to the 1820 story, Rip Van Winkle goes to sleep after bowling and drinking with a band of dwarves.
a. Rip awakens as an old man after sleeping how many years?
b. Who wrote this story?

20

Washington Irving

8. In French, this word refers to a person belonging to the conforming middle class; in Marxist theory, it relates to a member of the property-owning class, a capitalist. What's the word?

Bourgeois

9. Name the composers of these well-known operas:
a. Carmen
b. La Traviata
c. Hansel and Gretel

Georges Bizet
Giuseppe Verdi
Engelbert Humperdinck

10. What kind of baked pudding containing apples, raisins, and spices is named for a dark woman?

Brown Betty, also known as Apple Brown Betty

Party Round 10

1. On December 31 and January 1 of 2001, Ye Jiangchuan set a world record when he did this in China with 1004 people in 28 hours. What did he do?

Played chess simultaneously with 1004 people - and lost only one game!

2a. What general was defeated by the British at the Battle of Waterloo on June 18, 1815?
b. What British general defeated him?
c. In what country is Waterloo?

Napoleon

Duke of Wellington
Belgium

3. What revolving food tray is named for a lethargic woman?

Lazy Susan

4. Egyptian pharaohs claim to be descended from the Egyptian god of the sun, whose name is ... ?

Ra

5. Barbra Streisand directed and starred in this 1991 film in which she plays a psychiatrist dealing with Nick Nolte's demons. Name this film title, based on a novel by Pat Conroy.

Prince of Tides

6. One of the greatest celebrations ever seen in New York City occurred in May, 1883, when millions celebrated the completion of what engineering marvel?

Brooklyn Bridge

7. These islands were controlled by Great Britain since the 1830s, but in 1982 they were briefly occupied by Argentinean troops, leading to war, during which Britain gained victory.
a. Which island group is this?
b. Who was the British prime minister at the time?
c. The islands lie in what body of water?

Falkland Islands
Margaret Thatcher
Atlantic Ocean

8. Which Mexican-American labor leader, known for his commitment to nonviolent resistance, organized California food harvesters into the United Farm Workers in the 1960s?

César Chavez

9. According to John Gray's best-selling self-help book, men are from ...?, and women are from ... ?

Mars / Venus

10. In 1936, Hialeah in Florida was the world's first horse race track to make use of what new innovation?

Photo Finish

Party Round 11

1. Early film master Cecil B. DeMille created the same biblical epic twice: in 1923 and 1956. What is that film title?

The Ten Commandments

2. Sought for over 17 years in connection with a series of mail bombs, what mathematician was arrested in April, 1996 as the so-called Unabomber? (extra credit if spelled correctly)

Theodore Kaczynski

3. As the waters of the great flood receded, Noah's Ark supposedly came to rest on what mountain? Today located in what country?

Mt. Ararat / Turkey

4. Which best-selling author, who studied medicine at Harvard, created the TV series ER?

Michael Crichton

5. Which Danish navigator and explorer sailed in 1728 from the Pacific Ocean northward to the Arctic Ocean through the sea that now bears his name?

Vitus Bering (Bering Sea) proved, through his journeys, that Asia and North America are separate continents, though he did not realize it at the time

6. Which 15-year old American figure skater became Olympic champion in 1998, the youngest winner since Sonja Henie in 1928?

Tara Lipinsky

7. Identify these songs with "hello" in the title:
a. Popular hit by Louis Armstrong
b. Song written and recorded by the Beatles
c. Song with an edgy rhythm, recorded by the Doors

Hello Dolly
Hello, Goodbye
Hello, I Love You

8. The films The Bridges at Toko-Ri, the Manchurian Candidate, and M*A*S*H were all related to the same war. Which one?

Korean War

9. There are five modern Romance Languages. Three of them are Italian, French, and Spanish. Name the two other Romance Languages.

Portuguese / Romanian

10. Born in 1847 in Hungary, he grew to become an American journalist and publisher who eventually purchased the "New York Sun" and the "St. Louis Evening Dispatch" newspapers. Who was he?

Joseph Pulitzer

Party Round 15

1. Four of the children of which classical music composer also became noted musicians?

Johann Sebastian Bach

2. CD-ROM, a popular means of storing text, music, and visuals, is an abbreviation for what?

Compact Disc - Read Only Memory

3. During World War I she was a spy who worked for both the French and the Germans. In 1917 she was executed by the French. Today her name refers to a seductive double-dealing woman. Who is she?

Mata Hari

4. It is said that Erik the Red named this land incorrectly on purpose, in order to attract visitors and settlers. Which land?

Greenland

5. What is feldspar: a flower, a type of coral, or a mineral?

Type of rock-forming mineral

6. These are lines from songs. Give the song title:
a. In the Jungle, the Mighty Jungle

The Lion Sleeps Tonight

b. The day the music died
c. M.m.m.m.m.m.m.m.. - #1 hit of 1979

American Pie
My Sharona

7. What is the name for the female reproductive organ of a flower?

Pistil

8. When George Fox founded this religious organization in England in 1652, he warned his followers to "tremble at the word of the Lord." Which group was it?

Quakers

9. Name the artist who created each of the following:
a. The sculpture called The Pieta
b. The painting called Blue Boy
c. Female artist who painted Woman Bathing and Mother and Child

Michelangelo
Gainsborough
Mary Cassatt

10. What is the capital city of Libya?

Tripoli

Party Round 14

1. Why is February 2 a day of celebration in Punxsutawney, Pennsylvania?

It's Groundhog Day

2 . In January, 1994, Delta became the world's first airline to ban... what... on all its flights?

Smoking

3. What large, clumsy, flightless bird has been extinct for 200 years?

Dodo Bird

4. The whiskey called bourbon is distilled from a fermented mash composed at least 51% of what grain?

Corn

5. Which European explorer discovered the San Francisco Bay Area in 1579?

Sir Francis Drake

6. Which island lies west of Great Britain?

Ireland

7. What word describing a highly cultured person is named for a part of the head?

Highbrow

8. Which 20th century Italian educator established schools for young children based on helping develop their creation and accomplishment?

Maria Montessori

9. The Best Supporting Actor Oscar in a 1996 film went to an actor named after a Caribbean island. Which actor, which film?

Cuba Gooding, Jr. / Jerry Maguire

10. Name these these four-letter words:
a. The primary ingredient of beer
b. The war fought between British and Dutch settlers in South Africa
c. The 16th century Russian Czar famous for brutality toward his enemies

Malt
Boer

Ivan - the Terrible

Party Round 13

1. Can you identify three brands of automobiles, named after their creators, beginning with C?

Chevrolet / Citroen / Chrysler

2. Which person successfully led Nationalist armies against Loyalists in the 1930s Spanish Civil War, then ruled Spain until his death in 1975?

Generalisimo Francisco Franco

3. Nominated for the Academy Award as Best Picture from 1981 were Raiders of the Lost Ark, Chariots of Fire, On Golden Pond, and Reds. Which film won the Oscar?

Chariots of Fire - actor Ben Cross portrayed 1924 Olympic runner Harold Abrahams

4. The division of the United Nations that settles legal disputes, the International Court of Justice, is located in what city?

The Hague, Holland (Netherlands)

5. Which company in 1935 produced the first color photographic film: America's Kodak, Japan's Fuji, or Germany's Agfa?

Kodak

6. What is the French phrase for the overthrow of an existing government by a small group of people?

Coup d'etat (pronounced kooh day TAH)

7. To which sport or game does each of these terms refer?
a. T-bar
b. Kegling
c. Chuck-a-luck

Skiing
Bowling
Dice

8. This comic strip, created in 1931, is one of the most popular of all time. It was turned into films in the 1930s, 40s, 60s, and 90s. What is this comic strip created by Chester Gould?

Dick Tracy - the film in the 1990s stared Warren Beatty and Madonna

9. In the Atlantic or eastern Pacific Ocean this dangerous weather phenomenon is called a hurricane. What is it called in each of these locations?
a. The western Pacific Ocean
b. The Indian Ocean

Typhoon
Cyclone

10. According to Greek mythology, every time one of this dragon-like monster's heads was cut off, two more grew in its place. It was finally killed by Hercules. What was it?

Hydra

Party Round 12

1. Ludwig Van Beethoven was born in 1770 in which of these cities: Berlin, Bonn, or Bern?

Bonn, Germany

2. The earliest account of European travel to the far east was provided by what Venetian traveler who explored Asia from 1271 to 1295?

Marco Polo - His Travels of Marco Polo was the only written account of the Far East available to Europeans until the 17th century.

3. Which planet is named for the Roman god of the underworld?

Pluto

4. Arnold Schwartzenegger and a British actress both won Golden Globe acting awards for a 1994 comedy in which Arnold becomes pregnant. Name the film title and her name.

Junior / Emma Thompson

5. The U.S. Naval Academy and Army Military Academy are located in what two cities?

Annapolis, Maryland / West Point, New York

6. What three-word Latin phrase meaning "with highest praise or honor" represents the highest academic honor granted to a graduate?

Summa Cum Laude

7. What disease, caused by a deficiency of vitamin C, is characterized by bleeding gums and extreme weakness?

Scurvy

8. Think spies in literature:
a. Which writer wrote The Spy Who Loved Me, as well as other James Bond stories?

Ian Fleming

b. Which novelist wrote The Spy Who Came in From the Cold?

John le Carre

c. Which magazine featured the cartoon antics of Spy vs. Spy?

Mad Magazine

9. After passage of the 19th Amendment to the U.S. Constitution, in what year were women given the right to vote: 1880, 1900, or 1920?

1920

10. Louis (Satchmo) Armstrong was born July 4, 1900 in what city?

New Orleans

Party Round 16

1. What is the name of the repressive Islamic ruling party that controlled Afghanistan from the 1990s until 2001?

Taliban

2. Dick Cheney served in what position on the cabinet of President George H. Bush?

Secretary of Defense

3. The word aspirin is a generic term today, but in the 19th century it was a brand name for a new wonder drug developed by what company?

Bayer Pharmaceutical Company, of Germany

4. When she insured her legs for $1,250,000 in 1937, this movie star became known as "the girl with the million dollar legs." Who was she?

Betty Grable

5. What type of automobile was named for those 19th century covered wagons that carried passengers from the train station to their hotel?

Station wagon

6. In 1961, he was the first man launched into space. He was killed in 1968 while flying a routine aircraft training mission. Today he is buried within the Kremlin walls. Who is he?

Yuri Gagarin

7. Charlie Chaplin's most famous character appeared in 1914, in Chaplin's second big-screen appearance. Who was he?

The Little Tramp

8. Which person designed the U.S. monetary system, including the decimal system of dollars and cents, as well as the coins and bills we use today?

Thomas Jefferson

9. From the Olympics:
a. Just before World War II, the 1936 Olympics were held in which city?

Berlin

b. Which black U.S. athlete won four gold medals at those Olympics, dealing a blow to the Nazi notions of a master race?

Jesse Owens - in track and field events

10. Name the Shakespearean play:
a. Named after an Italian businessman

The Merchant of Venice

b. Named after a weather phenomenon
c. Named after an infant king of England

The Tempest
Henry VI

Party Round 17

1. May 14 is a national holiday in France, celebrated in honor of which woman?

Joan Of Arc

2. Which event in 1588 firmly established Britain as the world's leading naval power?

Defeat of the Spanish Armada

3. Which king of Mesopotamia, who lived from 1792-1750 B.C., put the laws of his country into a formal code?

Hammurabi

4. In which of these fields is a Nobel Prize not given: physics, mathematics, or literature?

Mathematics

5. The two Koreas are building a four-lane highway connecting their capital cities, which are... what?

Soeul / Pyongyang

6. Name these five-letter words:
a. Mushrooms, molds, and mildews
b. One of the founders of Rome
c. Clear, colorless fluid that fills the tissue spaces of the body

Fungi
Remus
Lymph

7. People named Anne. Give the last name:
a. She married William Shakespeare in 1582
b. She was half of the music group Eurythmics
c. She taught Helen Keller to read, write, and speak

Anne Hathaway
Annie Lennox
Anne Sullivan

8. The capital and largest city of Zaire is which of the following: Harare, Mombasa, or Kinshasa?

Kinshasa

9. What are these commonly used foreign words and phrases?
a. Have a good meal in French
b. Having amazing nerve, bordering on arrogance in Yiddish
c. A Russian political term meaning restructuring

Bon Appetit
Chutzpah

Perestroika

10a. Which rock music group recorded the campy hit song YMCA?
b. This group featured singers dressed as unusual characters, some of which were a soldier, a construction worker, and a biker. Name three others.

The Village People

Cowboy / Indian / Policeman

Party Round 18

1. Which intellectual wizard coined the proverb, "Genius is one percent inspiration and ninety-nine percent perspiration"?

Thomas Edison

2. If an airplane flies 100 miles due north, then turns and flies 100 miles directly northeast, how far is it then from the original starting point, to the nearest mile? margin 3 miles for calculation errors.

185 Miles

3. Global warming: The average temperature of the earth is about 57° Fahrenheit (14° centigrade). In the last 100 years the average global temperature has risen how many degrees Fahrenheit? 1, 2, or 4?

1 Degree Fahrenheit

4. The oldest person to win the Academy Award as Best Actor was 76 years old when he won in 1982. Who was he, and for what film did he win?

Henry Fonda / On Golden Pond

5. His history of the invasion of Greece by the Persian Empire was the beginning of all Western history writing. What ancient Greek historian is often called the father of history?

Herodotus

6. Each of these literary works became a film. Name the author:
a. 1939: Gone With the Wind
b. 1951: A Streetcar Named Desire
c. 1989: Hunt for Red October

Margaret Mitchell
Tennessee Williams
Tom Clancy

7. Which automobile company was established in 1899 in Torino, Italy?

Fiat

8. Queen Elizabeth's husband is the great-great-grandson of Queen Victoria. Who is he?

Prince Philip

9. America's first transcontinental airmail route connected what two cities in 1920?

New York / San Francisco

10. Which Italian composer wrote The Barber of Seville, and who is the title character?

Gioacchino Rossini / Figaro

Party Round 19

1. What seven-letter adjective is most commonly used to describe the exuberant and freewheeling decade of the 1920s?

Roaring

2. Which music superstar had seven consecutive #1 hits on the Billboard charts from 1985-1988: Madonna, Whitney Houston, Mariah Carey, or Janet Jackson?

Whitney Houston

3. What is the two-word name for the lowest prevailing interest rate that banks charge to corporations considered excellent risks?

Prime Rate

4. In 1932 she became the first woman to fly solo across the Atlantic Ocean. While attempting an around-the-world flight, she disappeared in the Pacific Ocean (1937) and was never heard from again. Who was she?

Amelia Earhart

5. The British Academy Award as best picture for 1994 went to what humorous film starring Hugh Grant and Andie MacDowell?

Four Weddings and a Funeral

6. Identify these people named Charles:
a. He wrote A Christmas Carol
b. He developed the Theory of Evolution
c. British general who commanded British forces in the American Revolution and surrendered to Washington in 1781

Charles Dickens
Charles Darwin
Charles Cornwallis

7. Which of these capital cities lies at the highest altitude: Salt Lake City, UT Denver,CO or Santa Fe, NM?

Santa Fe, 6,989 ft./ Denver, 5,282 ft. / Salt Lake City, 4,221 ft.

8. This American physician and army surgeon proved in 1901 that yellow fever is caused by a virus transmitted by mosquito. A medical center outside Washington, D.C. is named for him. Who is he?

Dr. Walter Reed (1851-1902)

9. When it was unveiled in 1982, one speaker at the ceremony said, "Thank you, America, for finally remembering us." What was it?

Vietnam Memorial in Washington, D.C.

10. In which 1992 film did Antonio Banderas and Armand Assante play brothers who flee Cuba with dreams of Latin music stardom in New York City?

The Mambo Kings

Party Round 20

1. Which beverage was named after its resemblance to the dark brown clothing warn by 16th century Italian monks?

Cappuccino from Cappucine monks

2. Which animal has the longest gestation period, up to a year and ten months?

Elephant

3. What language, now extinct, was spoken by the Goths, the tribe that invaded the Roman Empire?

Gothic

4. In 1940, seven months after the outbreak of World War II, Winston Churchill replaced which person as British prime minister?

Neville Chamberlain

5. What contracting membrane regulates the amount of light entering the eye? Is it the retina, iris, or pupil?

Iris

6. Which beautiful American city was laid out around 1800 by Pierre L'Enfant?

Washington, D.C.

7. In 1997, the Anxiety Disorders Association of America awarded Jack Nicholson for his role as an obsessive-compulsive, in which film?

As Good As It Gets

8. What are these three-letter words?
a. Religious philosophy that seeks enlightenment by meditation

Zen

b. An alcoholic liquor distilled from fermented molasses

Rum

c. A command given to a horse to turn to the right

Gee

9. He was America's first television superstar. His show, which ran from 1948 to 1956, attracted up to 80% of the TV audience. Who was he?

Milton Berle (Uncle Miltie)

10. In 1936, Ty Cobb, Honus Wagner, Babe Ruth, Walter Johnson, and Christy Mathewson were the first five ... what?

Members of Baseball Hall of Fame - Ty Cobb was the first player elected

Party Round 21

1. Which Republican candidate lost the 1996 Presidential election to William Jefferson Clinton?

Bob Dole

2. Which two musicians make up the pop music group Steely Dan?

Walter Becker / Donald Fagan

3. The most famous paintings of this French post-impressionist artist who lived from 1839-1906 include Mont Sainte-Victoire and The Card Players. Who is this artist?

Paul Cezanne

4. Who was Queen Elizabeth's father - the popular British king from 1936-1952?

George VI

5. How many Californias could fit inside Alaska? Closer to 2, 3, or 4?

Around 4

6. Which person, in the 1960s, accused the automobile industry of producing dangerous cars, when he wrote the book Unsafe at Any Speed?

Ralph Nader

7. In which Charles Dickens novel does Sydney Carton die on the guillotine in place of Charles Darnay, whom he resembles?

A Tale of Two Cities

8. Name these four-letter words:
a. A woodwind instrument
b. A secluded, wooded valley, or a computer maker
c. A cruel and destructive tribe from western Asia who conquered much of Europe in the fifth century

Oboe
Dell
Huns

9. This American theatrical producer is famed for his extravagant revues produced annually from 1907 to 1931. A film biography of his life won the 1936 Academy Award as Best Picture. Who was he?

Florenz Ziegfeld / Ziegfeld Follies / Film: The Great Ziegfeld

10. As you travel around the earth, each one-hour change in time zone occurs, on the average, after how many degrees of longitude?

$15°$ ($360°$ % 24 hours)

Party Round 22

1. What 1973 Supreme Court decision ruled that state laws restricting abortion violate women's right of privacy?

Roe versus Wade

2. He was easily elected president of his country in 1946, lost popularity after the death of his wife in 1952, and was overthrown in 1955 by a military coup. Who was this person, a two-time president of Argentina?

Juan Peron

3. This small item, designed to hold things together, was invented in 1858, and millions of millions of them have been sold ever since. What was it?

Safety Pin

4. What is the two-word title of the presiding officer of the British House of Lords?

Lord Chancellor

5. Geoffrey Rush won an Oscar in 1997 for his role as a troubled pianist. Name the film and the character he played.

Shine / David Helfgott

6. The first one of these ever constructed, complete with luxurious accessories and a piano, was built in Pittsburgh in 1905. The price of admission was 5¢. What was it?

Movie Theater / Nickelodeon

7. What type of musical composition is named after a state of ecstasy?

Rhapsody

8. Every devout Muslim must make a pilgrimage to Muhammad's home:
a. In which city?
b. What is this pilgrimage called in Arabic?
c. In 632 Muhammad died, in what city?

Mecca (Saudi Arabia)
Haj
Medina

9. Beale Street, famous for its blues clubs, is located in a black section of what U.S. city?

Memphis, Tennessee

10. Margaret Thatcher served as British prime minister from 1979 to 1990.
a. Which person preceded her in that position, from 1976 to 1979?
b. Who followed her, serving from 1990 to 1997?
C. Who followed him, serving from 1997?

James Callaghan

John Major
Tony Blair

Party Round 23

1. What new car line with a heavenly name was introduced by General Motors in 1990?

Saturn

2. Identify these movies whose titles contain the word cowboy:
a. 1969: Starring Dustin Hoffman and Jon Voight
b. 1980: Starring John Travolta and Debra Winger
c. 1989: Starring Matt Dillon and Kelly Lynch

Midnight Cowboy
Urban Cowboy
Drugstore Cowboy

3. The first Crusade began around the end of which century?

11th

4. On February 3, 1959, three beloved rock and roll music artists died in a cold, wintry air crash. Who were they?

Buddy Holly /Ritchie Valens / J.P Richardson (The Big Bopper)

5. What country lies directly north of Vietnam?

China

6. What happened in London in 1908 and 1948, Paris in 1900 and 1924, and Los Angeles in 1932 and 1984?

Summer Olympic Games

7. Coffee, which we take for granted today, was originally an exotic substance.
a. Coffee came to Europe from what part of the world?
b. The English word coffee is first recorded in 1601, evolving from what language?

Middle East
Arabic or Turkish - for qahveh, Ottoman pronunciation of Arabic qahwah

8. One Earth day is approximately 24 hours (actually 23'56). Which planet in our solar system has the longest day, equivalent to about 244 Earth days?

Venus

9. Alfred Nobel, who set aside $9 million in 1901 for annual prizes in important fields, gained his wealth and fame from what volatile business?

Explosives / Dynamite

10. Which Beatles song contains a verse sung in French?

Michelle (now sing that line!)

Party Round 24

1. Which New York Yankee hit his 500th career home run in 1965?

Mickey Mantle

2. Which American general and supreme commander of the Allied Expeditionary Force in World War II launched the invasion of Normandy in 1944 and oversaw the final defeat of Germany in 1945?

Dwight David Eisenhower

3. Name three member of the rock group The Eagles who had successful solo careers as recording artists

Glen Frey / Don Henley / Joe Walsh

4. What is the two-word name for the 630-foot high stainless steel arched structure built in the 1960s along the banks of the Mississippi River in St. Louis?

Gateway Arch - The Gateway to the West

5. In 1900, which German inventor designed and manufactured the first motorized, dirigible balloon?

Count Ferdinand Von Zeppelin 1838-1917

6. Most of the world's coffee is grown in countries that lie between the equator and the tropic of .... what?

Cancer

7. Who wrote each of these plays?
a. As You Like It
b. The Cherry Orchard
c. A Doll's House

Shakespeare
Anton Checkhov
Henrik Ibsen - 19th century Norwegian

8. Name these phrases containing the word Saint:
a. A U.S. state capital
b. A Breed of dog used by European monks to help patrol the snow-covered regions
c. The author of The Little Prince

St. Paul, Minnesota
St. Bernard
St. Exupery

9. Born in 1903, he became a singer and actor who received an Academy Award in 1944, and recorded 350 top 20 hit records, with more #1 hits than Frank Sinatra, Elvis Presley, and the Beatles! Who was he?

Bing Crosby

10. This mysterious number, the base of a natural logarithm, is related to natural and exponential growth. What is this number called, and what is its decimal value?

e - discovered by Swiss mathematician Leonhard Euler = approximately 2.72

Party Round 25

1. In which musical did Barbra Streisand sing Second Hand Rose?

Funny Girl

2. What game uses a deck of cards, a board with holes in it, and small wooden pegs?

Cribbage

3. Which two combating forces battled in the fifth century B.C. Peloponnesian War?

Greek City-States Athens and Sparta - Sparta won the war

4. Elvis Presley's first film, in 1956, was also the title of one of his first big musical hits. What was it?

Love Me Tender

5. The Greater Antilles are composed of Jamaica, Puerto Rico, Hispaniola, and what other island?

Cuba

6. Give the two-syllable names ending with the letter o for:
a. Comedian Julius Marx
b. Pupil of Socrates
c. Friend murdered by Macbeth

Groucho
Plato
Banquo

7. Name these five-letter words:
a. The best-selling book of all time
b. Very short African people, averaging less than 5 feet in height
c. The practice of charging more than the legal interest rate

Bible
Pygmy

Usury

8. Jesse Owen's world record in which sporting event stood from 1935 until 1960?

Long Jump

9. Because of her heroic and efficient work with wounded soldiers during the Crimean War in the 1850s, which woman is considered the founder of modern nursing?

Florence Nightingale (1820-1910)

10. In chemistry, acid will turn litmus paper what color?

Red

Party Round 26

1. What do we call a person or animal that lacks normal pigmentation, so that the skin and hair are unusually white?

Albino - Portuguese word, from albo, white, from Latin albus

2. What is the two-word name for the time around September 21 of each year when day and night are approximately equal in length?

Autumnal Equinox

3. Regarding Jack Nicholson films:
a. In what 1997 film did Jack Nicholson and Helen Hunt both win Oscars?

As Good As It Gets

b. What 1992 film starred Jack Nicholson, Demi Moore, and Tom Cruise?

A Few Good Men

c. In what 1970 film did Jack Nicholson, co-starring with Karen Black, play a once-promising pianist who had a fit over a chicken salad sandwich?

Five Easy Pieces

4. Among the greatest works of early Renaissance art are the bronze door panels called the Gates of Paradise created by 15th century sculptor Lorenzo Ghiberti for the cathedral in what artistic city?

Florence

5. What are the two most famous auction houses of London?

Sotheby's and Christie's

6. This ocean liner, launched in 1934 by the British, was their longest ship, the world's fastest ship, and still holds the record as the ship that has carried the most passengers. What is it?

Queen Mary - docked today in Long Beach, California as a floating hotel

7. What author first wrote the line, "Parting is such sweet sorrow"?

Shakespeare

8. Terry Gilliam is the only American member of what troupe of comedic performers?

Monty Python's Flying Circus

9. Which river rises in the Himalayas of Tibet and flows about 3,000 km through India and Pakistan into the Arabian Sea?

Indus River

10. One of the most important foods eaten by the American colonists was succotash, a dish composed of what two ingredients?

Sweet corn and beans - word of Native American origin

Party Round 27

1. What modern country is associated with each of these ancient civilizations?
a. Babylonian
b. Minoan
c. Hittite

Iraq
Greece
Asian Turkey or
Northern Syria

2. Which New Testament woman can be considered either a woman whom Jesus cured of evil spirits, or a repentant prostitute who washed the feet of Jesus?

Mary Magdalene

3. Words with food names that have nothing to do with food: Example: To encourage or incite to action: (Egg)
a. To lower yourself quickly to avoid something
b. To seek or gain favor by fawning or flattery
c. A legislative assembly in Japan

Duck
Curry
Diet

4. What is the sum of the atomic numbers of these three chemical elements: hydrogen, carbon, and oxygen?

15: H=1, C=6, O=8

5. In 1960, one was studying at the London School of Economics and the other at the Dartford Art School. They shared a mutual interest in rhythm and blues music and eventually formed one of the most popular groups of all time, the Rolling Stones. Who were they?

Mick Jagger /
Keith Richard

6. RCA and Columbia were the first two recording companies to produce music records made from what tough, flexible, shiny plastic?

Vinyl

7. The heaviest freshwater fish ever caught weighed 468 pound when caught in Benicia, California in 1963. What kind of fish was it?

White sturgeon

8. He established a tire factory in Akron, Ohio in 1900. His rubber research allied him with Henry Ford and Thomas Edison, planting rubber forests and at the same time searching for substitutes for natural rubber. Who was he?

Harvey Samuel
Firestone
(1868-1938)

9. Which King and Queen were executed by rebellious French citizens in 1793?

Louis XVI /
Marie Antoinette

10. According to the Bible, the final and conclusive battle between good and evil will take place in what place, whose name today symbolizes any great and decisive battle?

Armageddon

Party Round 28

1. What was the first artificial satellite, launched by the Russians in 1957?

Sputnik

2. One of the most successful business men in the world, Microsoft founder Bill Gates was a college drop-out from what university?

Harvard

3. In 1996 the U.S. Treasury Department introduced new counterfeit-proof paper money. What denomination of paper money was the first minted?

$100

4. Identify these people named John:
a. The March King
b. American industrialist who first manufactured mechanical plows around 1850
c. The most rejected suitor of all time

John Philips Sousa
John Deere
Dear John

5. Who were Richard Nixon's two vice presidents?

Spiro T. Agnew /
Gerald Ford

6. According to the Billboard Top 40 charts, based on radio play and record sales, the Beatles were the top performing musical group of the 1960s. Which group held this distinction in the...
a. 1970s?
b. 1980s?
c. 1990s?

Bee Gees
Hall and Oates
Boyz II Men

7. Meryl Streep received a 12th Oscar nomination for her role in what 1995 romantic film co-starring Clint Eastwood?

The Bridges of
Madison County

8. In which country did each of these sports originate?
a. Parachuting, early 20th century
b. Canoe racing, 1866
c. Croquet

U.S.A.
England
France

9. What is the name for the form of government controlled by a privileged, hereditary ruling class, generally resented by the lower classes?

Aristocracy

10. Three sisters have a total of $91. The first sister has 20% more than the second and the second sister has 20% more than the third. How much does the first sister have?

$36 ... 2nd has $30,
3rd has $25

Party Round 29

1. In the 19th century she helped women gain the right to vote. In the 20th century her likeness adorned an American coin. Who was she?

Susan B. Anthony

2. In the 2000 film Quills, which actor plays the role of what notoriously sadistic 18th century French author?

Geoffrey Rush / Marquis De Sade

3. Spoken by millions of people, Bengali is the primary language in what country?

Bangladesh

4. After the defeat of the Titans by Zeus, which mythological figure was condemned to support the Earth and sky on his shoulders for eternity?

Atlas - since the sixteenth century, pictures of Atlas and his burden have been used as decorations on maps. Accordingly, the world atlas is used for a book of maps

5. The Internet was born at the University of California in Los Angeles, in which of these years: 1959, 1969, or 1979?

1969

6. The world's largest empire covered the territory between the Danube River in Europe and China in the 13th century. Which person ruled this empire?

Genghis Khan

7. What part of the male anatomy (not female) is named after a character from the Bible?

Adam's Apple

8. Into what major body of water does each of these rivers flow?
a. Mississippi River
b. Jordan River
c. Europe's longest river, the Volga

Gulf of Mexico
Dead Sea
Caspian Sea

9. In the Middle Ages it was said they led to eternal punishment. These negative qualities are today known as the seven deadly sins. Some of them are: pride, greed, gluttony, envy. Name three other very important ones!

Anger / Lust / Sloth

10. Which TV journalist was the first female correspondent on the news program 60 Minutes?

Diane Sawyer

Party Round 30

1. In 1988, 160,000 people attended the largest rock music gathering ever held in East Germany. The Communist newspapers hailed which American rock performer as a friend of the working class?

Bruce Springsteen

2. The first names of these 20th century American jazz pianists and bandleaders were William and Edward, but they were better known by their noble nicknames. Who were they?

William "Count" Basie / Edward "Duke" Ellington

3. What was the first Arab nation to make peace with Israel?

Egypt

4. In 71 B.C. this escaped gladiator-slave led a revolt, defeating Roman armies along the way, but he was killed and many of his supporters were crucified. Almost 2,000 years later, in 1960, Kirk Douglas played his role on the silver screen. Who was he?

Spartacus, died 71 B.C.

5. These two U.S. cities grew the most (showed the largest absolute population increases) during the decade of the 1990's. They are in neighboring states and one is a capital city. Can you name them?

Las Vegas / Phoenix

6. Presidents Ronald Reagan and George W. Bush both promoted the development of a system to defend the U.S. against attack by enemies from outer space. What is the name of this initiative?

Star Wars Defense or Strategic Defense Initiative

7. Which unit of length, equal to one millionth of a meter, comes from the Greek word meaning small?

Micron

8. Which rare, colorless, gaseous element glows reddish orange when an electric charge passes through it?

Neon

9. As heavyweight champion of the world from 1937 to 1948, which boxer won 25 consecutive championship fights?

Joe Louis

10. A life-size statue of Pocahontas can be found in what Virginia city?

Jamestown, Virginia

Party Round 31

1. Speaking of food:
a. What do we call squid prepared as food?
b. What do we call the thick soup of vegetables, beans, pasta and herbs whose name comes from Italian, meaning to dish up or serve?

Calamari
Minestrone - from Latin ministrere, to serve food, from minister, servant

2. What pair of economic philosophers were the driving force behind communism when they wrote the 1848 book The Communist Manifest?

Karl Marx / Friedrich Engels

3. Which French existentialist writer declined the 1957 Nobel Prize for literature?

Jean Paul Sartre

4 a. This group of volcanic islands in the Pacific, known for their rare flora, their tortoises, penguins, and other unusual animals, are called the ... what... islands?
b. They are possessions of what country?
c. Which scientist visited the islands in 1835 and collected a wealth of scientific data on natural selection?

The Galapagos

Ecuador
Charles Darwin

5. Names or phrases beginning with La:
a. A sport
b. South American capital city
c. French explorer in North America

Lacrosse
La Paz, Bolivia
La Salle

6. Albert Einstein was living in what European capital city when he developed his Theory of Relativity?

Bern, Switzerland

7. What song, written by Paul Anka, was recorded by Frank Sinatra, Elvis Presley, and Sid Vicious, among others?

My Way

8. Novelists: I'll name the book, you name the author.
a. Bonfires of the Vanities
b. Brave New World
c. Dr. Zhivago

Tom Wolfe
Aldous Huxley
Boris Pasternak

9. What was the largest denominations of U.S. paper money ever printed: was it $1000, $5,000, or $10,000?

$10,000

10. Name these four-letter words beginning with F:
a. A small flute
b. An utter failure
c. Minor league baseball team

Fife
Flop
Farm club

Party Round 32

1. What word can refer to a donkey or a vain stupid person?

Ass

2. Which Albanian-born nun ran a leprosy clinic in India from 1950 until her death in 1997?

Mother Teresa

3. Which women won Academy Awards as Best Actress and Supporting Actress for their roles in the 1987 film, Moonstruck?

Cher / Olympia Dukakis

4. Colors: which basic colors come closest to each of the following?
a. Amethyst
b. Russet
c. Ocher

Purple
Brown
Orange-yellow

5. President Harry Truman liked to say, "If you can't stand the heat, get out of"... what?

The kitchen

6. Name the musicians:
a. 1960s British pop singer who recorded Wishin' and Hopin'
b. Saxophonist who recorded Just the Two of Us with Bill Withers
c. Singer and songwriter who co-wrote The Christmas Song (Chestnuts roasting...)

Dusty Springfield

Grover Washington, Jr.

Mel Torme

7a. As Asian culture becomes more popular throughout the world, which 5000 year old Chinese method of creating a harmonious environment is also gaining ground?
b. This system seeks to promote prosperity, good health, and general well being by examining the flow of energy, called what?

Feng Shui -Wind and Water (fung shway)

Qui (chee)

8. Which Swiss psychiatrist, founder of analytical psychology, created the concepts of extroversion and introversion?

Carl Jung (1875-1961)

9. Cartoon characters:
a. Who adopted Little Orphan Annie?
b. Who is Popeye's arch enemy, in love with Popeye's girlfriend?
c. What was Superman's boyhood home?

Daddy Warbucks
Bluto

Smallville

10. Which European company introduced the home video recorder in 1972?

Phillips

Party Round 33

1. Which person was sentenced to death in 1964 as a result of the assassination of President John F. Kennedy?

Jack Ruby, who shot and killed Lee Harvey Oswald, Kennedy's assassin

2. The first Nobel Prize for physics was awarded in 1901 to the German physicist who discovered a short-wave ray called the x-ray. People in many parts of the world refer to X-rays by his name. Who was he?

Wilhelm Roentgen

3. Which 19-20th century artist, son of the founder of a New York jewelry chain, applied the Art Nouveau style to stained glass windows, lamps, and other decorations?

Louis Tiffany

4. This ten-year old boy, son of King Henry VIII and Jane Seymour, became king of England and Ireland in 1547 and died of tuberculosis six years later. Who was he?

Edward VI

5. Places with unusual names. In which U.S. state are they located?
a. Walla Walla
b. Cucamunga
c. Keokuk

Washington
California
Iowa

6. In 1985, Olympic basketball star Lynette Woodward made history when she became the first female member of what professional basketball team?

Harlem Globetrotters

7. Which river in New Mexico and Arizona has the same name as a venomous lizard?

Gila Monster

8. Which young actress played the role of a crass-mouthed young prostitute in Martin Scorsese's 1976 classic film, Taxi Driver?

Jodie Foster

9. While working as a bouncer at a bar in Brooklyn, this hoodlum was knifed and got a scar on his cheek in a fight over a woman. Who was he?

Al Capone - called Scarface

10. Can you determine two numbers for which the sum of their squares is 628 and the difference of their squares is 340?

22 and 12

Party Round 34

1. In the late 1970s, which TV evangelist created the Moral Majority, a conservative pressure group opposed to abortion and homosexuality, and favoring school prayer and family values?

Jerry Falwell

2. Born Leslie Hope on May 29, 1903 in England, his friends in school called him Les Hope or Hopeless, so he changed his first name to what?

Bob Hope

3. The mental and physical exercise known as yoga evolves from what religion?

Hinduism

4. After his country gained independence from Britain in 1980, Robert Mugabe became the first Prime Minister of what nation?

Zimbabwe

5. a. Many of William Shakespeare's greatest plays were performed in what London theater?

The Globe

b. On which bank of which river does this theater lie?

South Bank Of Thames River

6. Gender-bending film roles:
a. In what 1993 film did Robin Williams play the role of a woman?

Mrs. Doubtfire

b. In what 1982 film did Dustin Hoffman play the role of a woman?

Tootsie

c. In what 1959 film did Jack Lemmon and Tony Curtis play the roles of women?

Some Like It Hot

7. One of the seven wonders of the ancient world is this 5th century B.C. statue built at Olympia, a colossal 40-foot high figure in gold and ivory, of whom?

Zeus / or Jupiter- all trace of it is lost

8. This musical piece for orchestra tells the story of a disobedient boy's encounter with a wild animal. Name the composer and the piece of music.

Peter and the Wolf / Sergei Prokofiev

9. The tallest mountain peak in the continental United States lies in a range with a Spanish name. Name the range and the peak.

Whitney in California, which lies in the Sierra Nevada range

10. Give the phrases containing the word Saint:
a. An alternate name for the city of Leningrad, Russia
b. The former prime time television hospital series
c. The 4th century Greek Bishop known for his kindness, who gave presents in secret to persons in trouble

St. Petersburg
St. Elsewhere
St. Nicholas

Party Round 35

1. One brother was first person to win Grammy awards for both classical and jazz recordings, the other hosted the band for the Tonight Show with Jay Leno. Who are these brothers?

Wynton / Branford Marsalis

2. All the parties that signed the 1998 Good Friday Agreement intended to work towards peace... where?

Northern Ireland

3. Name these phrases containing the number seven:
a. Little Dipper's contents
b. Christians who believe that the Second Coming of Christ is imminent
c. 1851 novel by the American writer Nathaniel Hawthorne

Seven Stars
Seventh Day Adventists
House of the Seven Gables

4. This plant was required growing in the middle ages. President Thomas Jefferson declared it a necessity; it was Kentucky's largest cash crop until 1915. What was it?

Hemp

5. In the 8th century, he was the first emperor of the Holy Roman Empire. Who is he?

Charlemagne. Also called Charles I or Charles the Great (742-814)

6. The 1. easternmost, 2. westernmost, 3. southernmost, and 4. largest countries of Africa all begin with the same letter. Name these countries.

1. Somalia
2. Senegal 3. South Africa 4. Sudan

7. Identify these people named John:
a. He shot Abraham Lincoln
b. This singer was born in Middlesex, England in 1947 with the name Reginald Dwight
c. This 17th century English poet who wrote Paradise Lost

John Wilkes Booth
Elton John

John Milton

8. Michael Jackson is one of how many children?

9 - he was 7th of 9

9. All rocks can be separated into three families. What are they?

Igneous, sedimentary, and metamorphic

10. When Michael Jordan retired from the Chicago Bulls for the first time in 1994, he signed a minor-league contract with what major league baseball team?

Chicago White Sox

Party Round 36

1. Whom did America's most famous widow, Jackie Kennedy, marry in 1968?

Greek businessman Aristotle Onassis

2. Which actor won the 1998 best supporting Academy Award for his work in A Fish Called Wanda?

Kevin Kline

3. Which emperor of Rome, around 300 A.D., was first to become a Christian?

Constantine I = Constantine the Great

4. What is James Bond's favorite adult beverage, and how does he like it served?

Martini /shaken, not stirred

5. In 1212 hundreds of children hoped to march from Germany to Jerusalem in the name of Christ. Most of them were sold into slavery or perished. By what two-word name do we call this historical event?

Children's Crusade

6. Which film starred Steve McQueen and Faye Dunaway in 1968, and Pierce Brosnan and Rene Russo in its 1999 remake?

Thomas Crown Affair

7. Capitals of South American countries:
a. Argentina
b. Ecuador
c. Uruguay

Buenos Aires
Quito
Montevideo

8. Which word, meaning fanatic, comes from the name of the first century Jewish group that fought against Roman rule in Palestine?

Zealot

9. Which Humphrey Bogart film won the Academy Award as Best Picture of 1943?

Casablanca

10. Considered the social and academic equivalent of the Ivy League schools, the Seven Sisters Colleges, created in 1915, were among the pioneers in higher education for women in the United States. Four of these colleges are Mount Holyoke, Barnard, Bryn Mawr, and Radcliffe. Name the other three.

Smith / Vassar / Wellesley

Party Round 37

1. Which British bacteriologist discovered penicillin in 1928 and won the 1945 Nobel Prize for his achievement?

Alexander Fleming

2. There were five comedy Marx brothers. Two of them were Groucho and Harpo. Who were the other three?

Chico / Zeppo / Gummo

3. Which U.S. President in 1823 declared that the United States would not tolerate European intervention in the Americas?

James Monroe-Monroe Doctrine

4. Use words beginning with M:
a. A dog of mixed or indeterminate breeding
b. The mixed Arab and Berber inhabitants of northern Africa
c. Lace work made by weaving cords into geometrical patterns

Mongrel
Moors

Macrame

5. I'll name the capital city, you name the country or region:
a. Belfast
b. Nairobi
c. Dhaka (Dacca)

Northern Ireland
Kenya
Bangladesh

6. That famous Hollywood sign above Los Angeles is one of the world's most recognizable landmarks, but when built in 1923, it had four more letters. What word was originally written there?

Hollywoodland- a housing development

7. Which pop music star was born Henry John Deutschendorf in Roswell, NM in 1943, and died in an air crash in the late 1990s near Monterey, California?

John Denver

8. Russian and several other Eastern European languages use what alphabet?

Cyrillic

9. Which major league baseball player holds each of these all-time career records:
a. Total hits, 4256
b. Most victories by a pitcher, 511
c. Highest career batting average, .367

Pete Rose
Cy Young
Ty Cobb

10. This prolific German composer wrote over 600 compositions, symphonies and works of chamber music in less than 20 years before he died of typhoid fever in 1828 at age 31. Who was he?

Franz Schubert (1797-1828)

Party Round 38

1. After his conquest in Asia, Julius Caesar made what three-word Latin announcement to the Roman senate?

Veni, Vidi, Vici (I came, I saw, I conquered)

2. Steven Spielberg won his first directing Oscar for his work in what 1994 film?

Schindler's List

3. Of the three political Kennedy brothers, John, Robert, and Edward, which was the youngest?

Edward (Teddie)

4. Which of these items became standard equipment on automobiles in 1909? Headlights, the rear view mirror, the windshield, or the electric starter?

Windshield

5. These are three of the world's earliest department stores:
a. Which was the world's first department store chain that was established in the 1920s and still exists today?

J.C. Penney's

b. What was London's first modern department store that was established in 1909?

Selfridge's

c. Established in Chicago in 1865, what was America's first department store?

Marshall Field

6. Two of the longest-running musicals in the London West end theater scene opened in 1981 and 1984 and feature the music of Andrew Lloyd Webber. What are they?

Cats / Starlight Express

7. This early TV program ran from 1947 to 1960; it was network TV's first weekday children's show, and NBC's first show broadcast in color. What was it?

Howdy Doody

8. The hypodermic syringe, a lifesaving devise used by doctors but abused by junkies, was invented at the time of which war?

American Civil War 1861-1865

9. Which is the rarest blood type: A, B, or AB?

AB

10. What is the area, to nearest whole number, of an equilateral triangle whose perimeter is 300 meters?

4330 sq. meters

Party Round 39

1. Born in 1606 in the Netherlands, this painter's masterpieces include The Anatomy Lesson of Dr. Tulp (1632) and The Night Watch (1642). Who was this painter?

Rembrandt van Rijn

2. Beloved actor and director Charlie Chaplin, accused of being a Communist sympathizer, left the U.S.A. in 1952 and settled in what country for the remaining 25 years of his life?

Switzerland

3. Who created the phrase, "Fifteen Minutes of Fame"?

Andy Warhol

4. What advisory group, composed of the commanders of the U.S. army, navy, air force and the marines, counsels the President on military affairs?

Joint Chiefs of Staff

5. The Bering Strait separates what two countries?

U.S.A. and Russia / Alaska and Siberia

6. What three words beginning with the letter P describe the ruling class, the common people, and the poorest class of ancient Rome?

Patricians / Plebeians / Proletariat

7. Napoleon was forced to step down as emperor of France as a result of a disastrous military campaign in the winter of 1812, in what country?

Russia

8. The heaviest crustacean ever captured was 3 foot 6 inches long and weighed 44 pounds. What kind of animal was it?

Lobster

9. The Academy Award winning film from 1935 was a sea adventure starring British actor Charles Laughton. What is the title?

Mutiny on the Bounty

10. This city of central Spain was an important Roman town, and its Roman aqueduct is still in use. A classical guitarist from Spain has the same name. Name the town or the guitarist.

Segovia, Andres

Party Round 40

1. One of the deadliest forms of vegetation is the death cap, which can kill a human who eats it in a few minutes. What form of vegetation is the death cap?

Mushroom / Fungus

2. Semitic is a descriptive term for certain peoples of the Middle East, including Jews and Arabs. The Semites are supposedly descended from the biblical Shem, the eldest son of which Bible figure?

Noah

3. Near what body of water, not far from what town, did Henry David Thoreau build a cabin in 1845 and live for more than two years?

Walden Pond / Concord, Massachusetts

4. "It was the best of times, it was the worst of times ..." are the first words of what 1859 novel, and who is the author?

A Tale of Two Cities / Charles Dickens

5. Which 14th century disease was appropriately named after the dark splotches it formed on its victims' bodies?

Black Death / Bubonic Plague

6. Phrases containing numbers:
a. Equally likely
b. Another name for the gambling game, Blackjack
c. An automotive drive system in which mechanical power is transmitted to all wheels

Fifty-fifty
Twenty-one
Four wheel drive

7. Founded in 1909, what is the oldest civil rights organization in the United States?

NAACP - National Association for the Advancement of Colored People

8. Which mountain range stretches almost 1,400 km. (850 mi.) along the length of Italy?

Appennines

9. These are quantities from physics:
a. Mass times acceleration
b. Work divided by time

Force
Power

10. This entertainer, born in 1912, earned four stars on the Hollywood Walk of Fame: one each for radio, television, movies, and records. He is a member of the Country Music Hall of Fame as well as the Cowboy Hall of Fame. Who is he?

Roy Rogers

Party Round 41

1. What word can refer to a place of transition for lost souls, or a Caribbean dance?

Limbo

2. Carol Channing won the Tony award as Best Actress for her role in one of Broadway's longest running shows. What was the title?

Hello Dolly

3. What organization won the Nobel Peace Prize at least 16 times?

International Red Cross

4. As a 7-year old child, he was invited to play violin at New York's Carnegie Hall. He grew up to become one of the world's great violin virtuosos, and he died in 1999. Who was he?

Yehudi Menuhin

5. If you buy 100 shares of a stock at $30, 200 shares at $20, and 300 shares at $10, then sell all at $15, did you make a profit or loss? What percent?

Loss Of 10% - paid $10,000 / sold for $9,000 = lost 10%

6. President George W. Bush's vice president, Dick Cheney, served in what position in the cabinet of President George H. Bush?

Secretary of Defense

7. Celine Dion recorded two songs that won the Academy Award as Best Song from a film. What are the song and film titles?

Beauty and the Beast 1991 / My Heart Must Go On, 1998 from Titanic

8. For which two National Basketball Association teams did all-time leading scorer Lou Alcindor/Kareem Abdul Jabbar play?

Milwaukee Bucks / Los Angeles Lakers

9. In 1943, French underwater explorer Jacques Cousteau helped create an invention designed for underwater breathing, and 60's British rock group Jethro Tull named an album after it. What is it?

Aqualung

10. The Treaty of Versailles officially ended World War I. Which French premier, British prime minister, and American president signed that treaty?

French Premier Georges Clemenceau, British Prime Minister David Lloyd George, U.S.. President Woodrow Wilson

Party Round 42

1. On May 18, 1980, this mountain in the Pacific northwest erupted after being dormant for 123 years. Which mountain is it?

Mount St. Helens

2. Mark Twain once said, "If you don't read the newspaper, you are uninformed; if you do read the newspaper, you are ..." what?

Misinformed

3. Actors who portrayed rock stars in films:
a. 1993 - Who played Tina Turner in What's Love Got To Do With It?

Angela Bassett, with Lawrence Fishburn as Ike

b. 1993 - Who played Jim Morrison in the Oliver Stone film The Doors?

Val Kilmer

c. 1997 - Who played the young Tejano singer assassinated by one of her fans in the film Selena?

Jennifer Lopez

4. Can you name four materials, considered almost as valuable as gems, and frequently used as jewelry, that come from plants and animals?

Coral / Pearl / Amber / Ivory

5. It is said that when Ernest Hemingway lived in Cuba in the 1940s, he would visit his favorite bar every day and consume up to a dozen of his favorite exotic cocktails, named for a Cuban city. Which drink?

Daiquiri

6. Born in 1943, he studied at Cambridge University, trained as a lawyer, played football for Real Madrid, won the 1968 Spanish Song Festival, and became one of the most popular singers in the world. Who is he?

Julio Iglesias

7. What is the name for the transparent outer covering of the front of the eye?

Cornea

8. What is Europe's oldest currency, dating back more than 2600 years?

Greek Drachma

9. Name the two most populous islands of Indonesia.

Sumatra / Java

10. The event that triggered World War I was the June 28, 1914 assassination of which person in what Yugoslavian city?

Archduke Francis Ferdinand and his wife / Sarajevo

Party Round 43

1. When a floating moth shorted out an early super computer, what new phrase was born?

Computer bug

2. Name three Spanish speaking countries beginning with the letter P.

Peru / Panama / Paragua

3. As a result of patriotism during the Gulf War, in 1991 Whitney Houston had an unlikely musical hit when she recorded what song?

Star Spangled Banner

4. Identify these people named Charles:
a. He flew The Spirit of St. Louis
b. A jazz trumpeter who recorded Feels So Good in 1978
c. The French writer who created Little Red Riding Hood

Charles Lindbergh
Chuck Mangione
Charles Perrault.

5. Which unusual characters were portrayed in the original 1966 film, Batman, by Burgess Meredith, Caesar Romero, Frank Gorshin, and Lee Meriwether?

Joker, Riddler, Penguin, Catwoman

6. February 25, 1964, young boxing phenomenon Cassius Clay first gained the heavyweight title when he knocked out which champion?

Sonny Liston

7. Some of her best-known works are Middlemarch, The Mill on the Floss, and Silas Marner. Her real name was Mary Ann Evans, but her pen name was ... what?

George Eliot

8. Name the common color that most closely approximates each of the following:
a. Hazel
b. Vermilion
c. Cerulean

Brown
Red to reddish-orange
Blue

9. In 1970, Dustin Hoffman was 33 years old when he played the film role of 121-year-old Jack Crabb in what film?

Little Big Man

10. In the 17-18th centuries he was employed by the British government to help stop piracy on the high seas, but he turned to piracy himself, was caught and executed in England. Who was he?

Captain William Kidd

Party Round 44

1. In what year did East and West Germany unify into the current Germany?

1990

2. What are these four-letter words:
a. To shed tears?
b. The active masculine cosmic principle in Chinese dualistic philosophy?
c. A man's full-legged suit and long coat popular during the early 1940s?

Weep
Yang

Zoot

3. Which too-skinny girl was the world's most famous model in 1967? ... and ... bonus point... what was her real name?

Twiggy / Leslie Hornby

4 a. For what 1983 film did Jack Nicholson win the Academy Award as Best Supporting Actor?
b. Which woman won the Best Actress Award for her role in the same film?

Terms of Endearment

Shirley MacLaine

5. The history of England began in 449 A.D., when Germanic peoples combine forces to conquer and banish the Romans from the British Isles. Name two of these tribes.

Angles / Saxons / Jutes (Jutland) / Anglo-Saxons

6. These frequent summer musical tours, exclusively composed of female performers such as Cheryl Crow, Paula Cole and the Dixie Chicks, have what name?

Lilith Fair, created by Sarah McLachlan

7. In what year were automobiles first sold in a choice of colors: 1913, 1923, or 1933?

1923 - at a Ford plant in France

8. Name the island:
a. Islands fought over by the Argentineans and the British in the 1980s
b. Island in the Mediterranean Sea on which Napoleon Bonaparte was born
c. Island shared by Haiti and the Dominican Republic

Falkland Islands

Corsica

Hispaniola

9. Give the two word phrases beginning with La:
a. Don Quixote's Spanish domain
b. Fashionable section of San Diego
c. Former New York mayor

La Mancha
La Jolla
Fiorello La Guardia

10. What are two names for the Greek and Roman gods of wine and nature?

Dionysus / Bacchus

Party Round 45

1. This person immigrated without money from Scotland to the United States in the mid 19th century. He made millions in the U.S. steel industry, and gave away most of the proceeds to educational, cultural, and peace-making organizations. Who was he?

Andrew Carnegie- he established free public libraries in many cities and established Carnegie Hall

2. For which 1980 film did Robert Redford win the Academy Award as Best Director?

Ordinary People

3. Words or phrases beginning with Go:
a. A desert in Asia
b. Patriotic song written by Irving Berlin
c. German author and philosopher who told the story of Faust

Gobi
God Bless America
Goethe

4. Place the Greek philosophers Plato, Aristotle, Socrates in historical order, starting with earliest.

Socrates / Plato / Aristotle

5. Versatile actress Meryl Streep won Best Actress Oscars in 1979 and 1982 for her roles in what films?

Sophie's Choice / Kramer vs. Kramer

6. How many of these world leaders were assassinated:
a. India leader Indira Gandhi?
b. Pakistani leader Benazir Bhutto?
c. U.S. President William Henry Harrison?

1 - only Gandhi

7. Which 2 types of rather small creatures are primarily responsible for having spread the bubonic plague that killed millions of people in Europe and Asia in the 14th century?

Rats and fleas

8. What did Newton Minow, the chairman of the federal communications commission, describe in 1961 as a vast wasteland?

Television

9. Which tennis player won the U.S. Open Tennis Tournament in 1974, 1976, 1982, 1983, 1984, and, to everybody's surprise, almost did it again in 1991 at the age of 39?

Jimmy Connors

10. The Hindu Kush mountain range extends 500 miles westward from Pakistan to what country?

Afghanistan

Party Round 46

1. Which TV series won the Emmy Award as best comedy five consecutive years in the 1990's?

Frasier, 1994 thru 1998

2. British explorer Richard Burton set out to Africa in 1858 to discover what?

Source of the Nile River - but he was not successful

3. The title of the Oscar-winning 1994 film contained the name of its primary, fictional character. What was it?

Forrest Gump

4. What are these phrases that have colors in them?
a. The stocks of the largest and most valuable companies
b. Organization whose logo is taken from the Swiss flag
c. Large possession of Denmark

Blue Chips
Red Cross
Greenland

5. Which book of the Bible records the deliverance of the Israelites from slavery in Egypt?

Exodus

6. Besides Mick Jagger, who were the other four members of the bad boy singing group, The Rolling Stones?

Keith Richards / Brian Jones / Bill Wyman / Charlie Watts

7. For her role in the 1939 classic, Gone With the Wind, she became the first African-American winner of an Oscar (Best Supporting Actress). Who was she?

Hattie McDaniel

8. Which 19th-century American publisher compiled the first standard reference work for quotations?

John Bartlett

9. The headquarters of the NATO, North Atlantic Treaty Organization, is located in which country?

Belgium

10. The Treaty of Versailles officially ended World War I. Which French premier, British prime minister, and American President signed that treaty?

French Premier Georges Clemenceau, British Prime Minister David George, and U.S. President Wilson

Party Round 47

1. His doctor gave him less than 50% chance of survival from cancer. He not only kicked the disease, but he won bicycle's Tour de France numerous times. Who is he?

Lance Armstrong

2. Born in New York City, her career began in 1961 when she won a New York talent contest. In 1962 she made her Broadway debut, in 1964 her movie debut, and in 1968 she won an Oscar. Who is she?

Barbra Streisand- Best Actress for her performance in Funny Girl

3. The system of air-mail began in 1909, when letters were transported by airplane between which two countries?

England and France

4. The invention of the match for starting fires was made possible about 1680, when scientists realized that two chemical elements, when rubbed together, would burst into flame. Which two elements?

Phosphorus / Sulfur

5. In 1955 Martin Luther King received a doctorate degree from Boston University, in what subject area?

Theology

6. This 17th century French cardinal and political leader was the chief of government under King Louis XIII. He established absolute monarchy in France and broke the political power of the Huguenots (French Protestants). Who was he?

Cardinal Richelieu

7. What visible electric discharge on the mast of a ship or the wing of an airplane during an electrical storm is named after the fourth-century patron saint of sailors, and is also the title of a 1985 movie starring Rob Lowe and Demi Moore?

St. Elmo's Fire

8. Who are these people with geographical names?
a. He sang "Take me home, country roads.."
b. A swashbuckling actor who played Robin Hood in 1922, and his son played Gunga Din in 1939
c. A supermodel born 1963 in Santa Barbara, California

John Denver
Douglas Fairbanks

Kathy Ireland

9. The longest-serving leader of any Asian country lead Indonesia from 1967 until 1999, when forced out of office by the citizens. Who is he?

Suharto

10. What is a hemi-demi-semi-quaver?

A musical note: 64th note

Party Round 48

1. What is a two-word name for the spicy Middle-Eastern food dish consisting of meat and vegetables roasted on skewers?

Shish Kebab

2. In 1963 Valentina Tereshkova became the first woman to go where no woman had ever gone before. Where?

Into Outer Space: she was an astronaut

3. The song Yesterday was released on which Beatles album?

Help!

4. In what year did the sales of music on CD first exceed those of cassettes and vinyl records put together? Was it 1992, 1994, or 1996?

1992

5. Original inhabitants of South Africa, these nomadic hunters and gatherers of the Kalahari Desert were named by Dutch settlers after their native environment. Who were they?

Bushmen

6. Many European nations begin with the letter S. Some are Spain, Sweden, and Scotland. Can you name three more?

Any three of Switzerland / Slovakia / Slovenia / San Marino

7. Eminent domain is the right of the government to do what?

Take private property for public use (with reimbursement) (for example, to build a highway or railroad)

8. What were the first two NFL teams to play in four Super Bowl games without a victory?

Buffalo Bills / Minnesota Vikings

9. Margaret Hamilton received a 1939 Oscar nomination as Best Supporting Actress for what role in the film The Wizard of Oz?

Wicked Witch of the West

10. What part of speech is the word "the"? (2 word answer)

Definite article-whereas "a" and "an" are indefinite articles

Party Round 49

1. She has been a movie star, sex-symbol, political activist, athletic freak, and born-again Christian. Who is she?

Jane Fonda

2. Which 19th century French chemist, who discovered that diseases are caused by microorganisms, is considered the founder of modern microbiology?

Louis Pasteur (1822-1895) / invented the process of pasteurization, and developed vaccines for anthrax, rabies, and chicken cholera

3. These composers' names begin with S:
a. The Waltz King
b. His best-known instrumental work was Unfinished
c. A 19th century German romantic pianist and composer

Johann Strauss
Franz Schubert
Robert Schumann

4. This 18th century radical French political leader helped execute thousands of people without trial during the Reign of Terror. After a public reaction against his extreme policies, he was executed without trial himself. Who was he?

Robespierre

5. The first starring role for both Richard Benjamin and Ali MacGraw came about in which 1969 film based on a Philip Roth novel?

Goodbye Columbus

6. What are the two most widely spoken languages in Africa?

Any two of Arabic / Swahili / Hausa, each with more than 20 million speakers

7. Which two rivers with state names form the southern border of Illinois?

Mississippi / Ohio

8. These phrases are related to the moon:
a. Ralph Kramden said it to his wife, Alice in the T.V. series The Honeymooners.
b. Drummer of The Who, who died of a drug overdose in 1978
c. The title of David Niven's autobiography

"You're going to the moon, Alice!"
Keith Moon

The Moon's a Balloon

9. Her parents were Zeus and Leda. Legend has it that her exceptional beauty caused the Trojan War. Who was she?

Helen of Troy who was abducted by Paris

10. If the population of a city grows at 10% per year, it will double in approximately how many years? (to nearest year)

7 years

Party Round 50

1. What does an ornithologist study?

Birds

2. These phrases have numbers in them:
a. The world's poor and undeveloped nations
b. To refuse to self-incriminate oneself in a court trial
c. A new surge of energy after a period of mental or physical exhaustion

Third World
Fifth Amendment
Second Wind

3. This Academy-award winning actor played the 1980 film role of a boxer. Name the actor, the athlete, and the film title.

Robert DeNiro / Jake Lamotta / Raging Bull

4. From 1895 until 1958, the French controlled a number of countries in the western part of what continent?

Africa

5. This British pop musician, born in 1940, had dozens of hits in Britain, but never met with great popularity in the U.S.A. He is sometimes called the Elvis of England. Who is this superstar of British rock music?

Cliff Richard

6. What city is capital of Australia's Victoria state?

Melbourne

7. The well-known line, "Their's is not to reason why, Their's but to do and die," comes from the English poem, The Charge of the Light Brigade, written by whom?

Alfred, Lord Tennyson

8. Events in years ending with 8:
a. Legalized gambling was introduced in Atlantic City.
b. The first Disney animated film with sound, Steamboat Willie, was released.
c. U.S. performed its last nuclear tests in the Pacific Ocean.

1978
1928
1958

9. Which constellation in the southern sky has the same name as an organization containing many intelligent people?

Mensa

10. Football fans in 1999 were saddened by the death of the NFL's all-time leading rusher, called sweetness for his smooth moves and pleasant nature. Who was he?

Walter Payton

Party Round 51

1. Which artist's first important painting, from 1885, was called The Potato Eaters?

Vincent Van Gogh

2. What is the tropical tree whose seeds are used to make chocolate?

Cacao

3. Most commercial jets take off and land at about the same speed. What is that speed? (margin 20 miles per hour or 30 km per hour)

160 miles per hour / 260 km per hour

4. What television show, popular in the 1970s and 1980s and named after a woman, holds the record for winning the most Emmy Awards by a TV series?

Mary Tyler Moore Show - Won 29 Emmy Awards

5. What stuffed toy bear and what little boy owner appear in several children's books written by English author A.A. Milne?

Winnie-the-Pooh and Christopher Robin

6. In this 1992 film comedy, Nicholas Cage loses his fiancee played by Sara Jessica Parker in a Las Vegas poker game to mobster James Caan, and a corps of "flying Elvises" helps him rescue her. What is the film title?

Honeymoon in Vegas

7. The Mogul Empire thrived from the 16th to the 18th Centuries, primarily in which country?

India

8. Name two important possessions that people burned in the late 1960s and early 70s as a form of political protest or social liberation?

Draft cards / Bras

9. Which London landmark is named after Sir Benjamin Hall, British Commissioner of Works in the 1850s?

Big Ben

10. Which lake, the world's deepest, contains one-fifth of Earth's fresh water?

Lake Baikal, in Siberia - depth of 5,700 ft (1,740 meters)

Party Round 52

1. What is a septuagenarian?

Someone 70 years old or between the ages of 70 and 80

2. Can you name three composers of classical music whose last names begin with R?

Rachmaninov, Rimsky-Korsakov, Rossini

3. Which U.S. President negotiated the Camp David accords that lead to a signed peace treaty between Egypt and Israel?

Jimmy Carter, 1979

4. Around 1990, which rebellious Irish singer tore up a photo of a pope on Saturday Night Live?

Sinead O'Connor

5. He was born in 1934 in Canada and his son was born in 1967 in London, England. Both father and son grew up to be popular actors. Who are they?

Donald and Kiefer Sutherland

6. Ships traveling from the Atlantic to the Pacific Ocean (or vice versa) must pay about $50,000 to do what?

Pass through the Panama Canal

7. The Bullfinch Pub in Boston is better known to television fans by what name?

Cheers

8. Which automobile pioneer is credited in 1886 as manufacturing the first vehicle powered with an internal-combustion engine?

Karl Friedrich Benz

9. Which 19th century horror novel was written by Mary Shelley?

Frankenstein

10. Name the color that most closely approximates each of these:
a. Azure
b. Sepia
c. Fuchsia

Blue
Brown
Purple

Party Round 53

1. What is the Holy See?

The Vatican / jurisdiction of the pope

2. What gas is most commonly used in refrigeration and air conditioning?

Freon

3. The Academy award-winning best actress from 1980 played the film role of "the first lady of country music." Name the actress, the film, and the singer portrayed in the film.

Sissy Spacek / Coal Miner's Daughter / Loretta Lynn

4. What word can refer to a soft, creamy European cheese, or to the fundamental units of matter, smaller than an electrons (as surmised by scientists).

Quark

5. Which U.S. President was assassinated in 1901?

William McKinley

6. He is the son of a Philadelphia Phillies pitcher. His wife comes from Star, Mississippi. Together this country music couple sold more than 30 million records and won numerous awards through the 2000s. Who are they?

Faith Hill / Tim McGraw -Father Tug McGraw, baseball player

7. What historically significant event occurred in England from 1642 to 1648?

Civil War between the Parliamentarians and Royalists

8. One of the best selling perfume fragrances of all time was introduced in 1921 by a French fashion designer who named it after herself. Which fragrance?

Gabrielle Bonheur Chanel, known as Coco

9. What simple fraction has a decimal value of .0625?

1/16

10. The name of what musical instrument comes from Greek words meaning wood and sound?

Xylophone

Party Round 54

1. Who was the last leader of the U.S.S.R.?

Mikhail Gorbachev

2. What European country suffered a civil war from 1936-1939?

Spain

3. What 18th century British navigator and explorer charted and named many islands of the Pacific Ocean.

Captain James Cook (1728-1779)

4. The Navajo Indian reservation covers over 16 million acres, primarily in what three U.S. states?

Arizona / New Mexico / Utah

5. In 1978, a museum in West Germany spent $1.8 million to buy a single book. What was it?

Gutenberg Bible, first book printed with moveable type

6. Which fast-food chain lost more than $29 million after their hamburgers were linked to deadly bacterial outbreaks in 1993?

Jack in the Box

7. In the first celebrity fund-raiser, in 1971, musical stars Eric Clapton, Bob Dylan, and Ringo Starr joined event coordinator and former Beatle George Harrison to raise money for hungry residents of what starving nation?

Bangladesh

8. Which 19-year old boxer became, in 1986, the youngest ever to win the heavyweight title?

Mike Tyson

9. Which of these body parts is NOT located in the abdomen: the stomach, intestines, kidney, or liver?

Kidney

10. Let's say a slot machine contains three independent spinning reels; each reel has 10 symbols and 3 of them are winners. What's the probability that all three reels will turn up a winner? (write answer as a percent).

.3 to the power 3 = .027 = 2.7%

Party Round 55

1. What do we call the Eastern medical technique in which thin needles are inserted into the body to relieve pain?

Acupuncture

2. What island of Indonesia is sometimes called the Jewel of the East

Bali

3. Who created these warm and fuzzy phrases?
a. Happiness is a warm puppy

Charles Schultz / Snoopy

b. Happiness is a warm gun

The Beatles

4. Oliver Stone won the Academy Award as Best Director twice in a four year span: for a 1986 film and a 1989 film, both related to the same subject. What were the film titles?

Platoon / Born on the Fourth of July - Vietnam War

5. This former first lady is remembered for her calmness in the face of a British invasion of Washington, D.C. during the War of 1812. When the British burned the White House in 1814, she saved many documents, including a portrait of George Washington by Gilbert Stuart. Who was this presidential wife?

Dolly Madison

6. This 1946 book, written by 43-year old New York psychiatrist, became the best-selling baby book of all time. What's the title and who wrote it?

The Common Sense Book of Baby and Child Care, re-titled Baby and Child Care / Benjamin Spock

7. Name that sugar:
a. The most common form of sugar, found in the bodies of animals and plants

Glucose

b. Sweetest type of sugar, occurring in fruits and honey

Fructose

c. Extracted from sugar cane and beets and used as table sugar

Sucrose

8. Which romantic British poet, about 200 years ago, wrote, "Water, water, everywhere, nor any drop to drink...": Browning, Byron, or Coleridge?

Samuel Taylor Coleridge

9. He excelled in five sports at Syracuse University in the 1950s and '60s and became one of the greatest players in the NFL, but retired at his peak to pursue a Hollywood movie career. Who was he, and with what NFL team did he play?

Jim Brown / Cleveland Browns - worked in films, as The Dirty Dozen and I'm Gonna Git You Sucka!

10. 39,370 inches is equivalent to what unit of distance?

One kilometer

Party Round 56

1. Which 17-18th century monk invented sparkling champagne, and later the cork stopper?

Dom Perignon

2. He was Hollywood's first million-dollar superstar. He signed a contract in 1917 to direct and star in eight films. Who was he?

Charlie Chaplin

3. During the war of 1814 an American lawyer and poet wrote a poem that was set to music and renamed The Star-Spangled Banner. Who was he, and where was he when he wrote it?

Francis Scott Key / Fort McHenry in Baltimore

4. Name the U.S. president whose encouragement of business speculation lead the stock market from boom to bust in 1929?

Calvin Coolidge (1872-1933)

5. Which Russian author wrote Crime and Punishment as well as The Brothers Karamazov?

Fyodor Dostoyevsky

6. Name the lead singers of these music groups:
a. 1950s: The Crickets
b. 1970s: The Bee Gees
c. 1990s: Hootie and the Blowfish

Buddy Holly
Barry Gibb
Darius Rucker

7. John Grisham's first successful novel, The Firm, was turned into a big-screen film in 1991. Which actor played the lead role of the young lawyer who outwits the big evil legal firm?

Tom Cruise

8. What British actor and director of the National Theatre of Great Britain, knighted in 1947, is well known for his Shakespearean interpretations?

Sir Laurence Olivier - Laurence Kerr, Baron Olivier of Brighton (1907-1989)

9. What unit of electricity is defined as the work done when a current of 1 amp is passed through a resistance of 1 ohm for 1 second? Is it a volt, a watt, or a joule?

Joule

10. The first modern Olympic Games, in 1896, took place in Athens, Greece (appropriately).
a. The second Olympic Games were held in 1900, in what city of Europe?
b. The third Olympic Games were held in 1904, in what quickly-growing midwestern city of the U.S.A.?

Paris

St. Louis, Missouri

Party Round 57

1. In which two countries can you ski the Alps and swim in the Mediterranean?

France / Italy

2. In 1729, the Chinese banned the smoking of what product?

Opium

3. What three nations joined forces in 1707 to form the United Kingdom of Great Britain?

England / Scotland / Wales ... Ireland joined in 1801

4. In which 1983 film did Meryl Streep play the true-story role of a nuclear factory employee who risks her life to protect workers from safety hazards?

Silkwood

5. What two chemical elements are most commonly used as disinfectant or antiseptic?

Iodine / Chlorine

6. What's the next line of this poem by boxer Muhammad Ali: "His hands can't hit what his eyes can't see"...?

Floats like a butterfly, stings like a bee

7. Which product, well-known for its humorous advertising, was advertised in the 1960s with the two slogans: "Small Wonder" and "Relieves Gas Pains"?

Volkswagen

8. Which 20th century American painter gained fame by dripping or pouring swirls and spatterings of paint on a canvas?

Jackson Pollock

9. According to the proverb, what is the Mother of Invention?

Necessity

10. In a non-leap year, what month and date can be called the exact middle day of the year?

July 2 - 182 days before it, 182 days after it

Party Round 58

1. Brad Pitt starred as a seeker of spirituality in the Himalayas in what 1997 film?

Seven Years in Tibet

2. The second wife of King Henry VIII was convicted of adultery and beheaded. Who was this woman, the mother of Queen Elizabeth I?

Anne Boleyn

3. Which gun manufacturing company was started by an Italian family in 1550, and still bears their name today?

Beretta

4. In 1964 a phenomenal female group from Detroit hit the pop music scene, and their first #1 hit contained a question in the title. What group and what song title?

The Supremes / Where Did Our Love Go?

5. Which Norman conqueror proclaimed himself king of England after defeating the English King Harold at the Battle of Hastings in 1066?

William the Conqueror

6. In this 1865 classic novel, a minor thief tries to bury his past and become a respectable town mayor, but the police inspector won't let him. Name the novel and the author.

Les Miserables / Victor Hugo (1802-1885)

7. Name the lead singers of these music groups:
a. 1960s: Herman's Hermits
b. 1980s: Wham
c. 1990s: Nine Stories

Peter Noone
George Michael
Lisa Loeb

8. Originally called Military Patrol, it combines cross-country skiing and rifle shooting and became a winter Olympic sport in 1960. What is it?

Biathlon

9. Who was the first black manager of a Major League baseball team?

Frank Robinson

10. A Rubik's cube is composed of 27 equal sized blocks, colored on the outside. Some are colored on three sides, some two sides, some one side. How many of these blocks have colors on one or two sides only?

18

Party Round 59

1. In this 1940s play, a salesman named Willy Loman feels useless in his occupation and kills himself. What is the title of this play and which husband of Marilyn Monroe wrote it?

Death of a Salesman / Arthur Miller

2. What short word can refer to a cooking utensil, a bad movie review, or a search for gold?

Pan

3. The custom of fooling friends and relatives on the first of April began in the late 1500s in which country: Holland, France, or Italy?

France

4. Famous for his beret, be-bop sunglasses, and his trumpet whose horn points diagonally upward toward the heavens, who was this jazz all-star who died in 1993?

Dizzy Gillespie

5. Which homosexual, cross-dressing, British heroin junkie was one of the world's most popular pop-music personalities of the 1980s and 1990s?

Boy George, leader of Culture Club and solo artist

6. Which word can mean all the following: to rain, to cause an event to happen, and to separate a solid from a chemical solution?

Precipitate

7. In June, 1215, the English King John authorized a list of rights and privileges for the common person.
a. What was this early constitution called?
b. At which meadow in southeast England along the Thames River did he sign it?

The Magna Carta
Runnymede

8. In the 1980 film Raging Bull, Robert DeNiro played the role of which boxer?

Jake La Motta

9. The world's first lawn tennis championship was contested in 1877, where?

Wimbledon

10. On a recent shopping trip, Julie spent 85% of her money, and now has $75 left. How much did she spend?

$425 of $500

Party Round 60

1. Which song features the words, "Newspaper taxis appear on the shore"?

Lucy in the Sky with Diamonds

2. The First Amendment to the Constitution guarantees freedom of speech, religion, press, etc. What does the Second Amendment primarily provide?

A well regulated militia, being necessary to the security of a free state, the right of the people to keep and bear arms, shall not be infringed

3. The English ports of Plymouth, Southampton, and Dover all lie on what body of water?

English Channel

4. What are the only two countries of South America that do not border Brazil?

Ecuador and Chile

5. In what 1989 Spike Lee film does Danny Aiello play a Brooklyn pizzeria owner involved in a racial conflict?

Do the Right Thing

6. Since the first World Cup of soccer football in 1930, which two European teams have been in the final game most frequently?

Germany / Italy

7. Britain's highest military award, given for conspicuous valor, is named after a queen. What is it?

Victoria Cross

8. How is it possible to determine the sex of a parakeet?

By the color of the wax-like swelling on the beak, called the cere

9. At least how old is three-star brandy: three years, five years or fifty years?

Five years

10. Which 20th Century political leader's motto was, "Never Give In. Never Give In. Never. Never. Never."?

Winston Churchill

Party Round 61

1. The average person in the world consumes about 2,700 of these per day. What are they?

Calories

2. What was the tenth month of the Roman year?

December

3. The Winter Olympic Games were held in Asia only two times, in what two cities?

Nagano / Sapporo, Japan

4. What empire controlled much of the Western World from the 14th-20th century?

Ottoman empire centered in Constantinople (Istanbul), Turkey

5. On February 9, 1964, seventy three million people watched the same TV broadcast, earning it the highest ratings in TV history up to that time. What television show, featuring what music act, generated all this excitement?

Beatles first appeared on Ed Sullivan television show

6. Well-known around the end of the 1980s:
a. Spicy actress who plays a steamy singer in The Fabulous Baker Boys, initials M.P.

Michelle Pfeiffer

b. High-fashion designer easily recognized by her initials DKNY

Donna Karan

c. Artist who shocks the art world and political conservatives with his explicit photography, initials R.M.

Robert Mapplethorpe

7. Which informative Web site was named after the fictional servant of P.G. Wodehouse novels?

Ask Jeeves

8. Most painting students learn this list: the three primary colors of paint, the ones that can form any colors when mixed. What are they?

Blue / red / yellow (Not blue, red, green - these are primary colors of light)

9. One of the most popular medicines of all time, Viagra, was introduced in April, 1998 by what pharmaceutical company?

Pfizer

10. Which young actress and star of the television series Ally McBeal has a Greek first name that means most beautiful?

Calista Flockhart

Party Round 62

1. Name the authors of each of these works of literature:
a. Atlas Shrugged, and The Fountainhead
b. The classic, Little Women
c. The novel turned TV series: Brideshead Revisited

Ayn Rand
Louisa May Alcott
Evelyn Waugh

2. In September, 1997, Vice President Al Gore met with Hollywood movie and television executives, urging them to curb the increased display in movies and TV of ... what?

Smoking

3. Leonardo Da Vinci was born in what year ending with 52?

1452, and died in 1519

4. What's the area of a square whose diagonal is one hundred inches long?

50 square meters

5. Which male and female actors co-starred in the Academy-award winning comedy-drama, American Beauty?

Kevin Spacey / Annette Bening

6. What is the most populous city in Scotland?

Glasgow

7. Which song features the line "I've been terribly alone and forgotten in Manhattan"?

I Left My Heart in San Francisco

8. Which principal states, "If something can go wrong, it will, and usually at the worst time"?

Murphy's law

9a. Covered only by her long hair, Lady Godiva rode naked on horseback through the streets of what English city?
b. Why? (3 words or less)

Coventry

Tax protest

10. Julia Roberts films: I'll begin the title, you finish it:
a. 1999: Notting...
b. 1989: Steel...
c. 1988: Mystic...
d. 2001: America's...

Hill
Magnolias
Pizza
Sweethearts

Party Round 63

1. Questions about Easter:
a. Which person's betrayal led to the arrest and crucifixion of Jesus?

Judas Iscariot

b. Jesus was turned over to the which Roman governor to be crucified?

Pontius Pilate

c. Roman soldiers placed what on his head?

Crown of thorns

2. Since the early 1700s, virtually all British prime ministers have lived at what London street address?

Number 10 Downing Street

3. Identify two European capital cities whose names can be spelled with exactly four letters.

Bern, Switzerland / Oslo, Norway

4. According to research by a New York newspaper into personal ads (men seeking women, women seeking men), who is more likely to place personal ads: men or women?

Men

5. In 1996 an American musician gathered some of the greatest names of Cuban music to record a musical album and a film. The album won Grammy Awards and the movie had worldwide success. Name the film title and the musician who made it happen.

Buena Vista Social Club / Ry Cooder

6. In 1967, who was the first black judge to hold a seat as a justice of the U.S. Supreme Court?

Thurgood Marshall

7. Towards the end of the 20th century, the FBI referred to what American city as the Bank Robbery Capital of the World?

Los Angeles

8. Which month of the year is named for the Roman god of gates and doorways, depicted with two faces looking in opposite directions?

January / named after Janus

9. On September 18, 1851 the New York Times published its first issue, and introduced what long-standing motto?

All the News That's Fit to Print

10. What type of reference book is named after a character from Greek mythology?

Atlas

Party Round 64

1. What 17th century French king, who built the magnificent Palace of Versailles, called himself the Sun King and adopted the sun as his emblem?

Louis XIV

2. What unloved product is created when sunlight reacts with hydrocarbons and nitrogen oxides?

Smog byproducts of automobile emissions and factories

3. According to the U.S. Constitution, no U.S. soldier can ever be quartered, without permission, where?

In any citizen's home

4. Pride, greed, lust, anger, gluttony, envy, and sloth are collectively known as what?

Seven deadly sins

5. The largest selling single record of all time, released in 1942, has sold tens of million of copies worldwide, even though it's only popular a few weeks each year.
a. What's the song title?
b. Who was the recording artist?
c. What Jewish composer wrote the song?

White Christmas
Bing Crosby
Irving Berlin

6. Working in a government-sponsored program, computer scientists at two California Universities made history in 1969 when they exchanged information long-distance by computers. This was the beginning of the Internet as we know it. Which two California universities were involved?

UCLA and Stanford / early name for the Internet was Arpanet

7. What two cities of the world have the most Koreans?

Seoul / Los Angeles

8. How many humans were on Noah's ark?

8, Noah, his wife, their three sons and their wives

9. Which well-known cartoon characters were created by each of the following artists?
a. Matt Groening
b. Scott Adams
c. Chester Gould

Simpsons
Dilbert
Dick Tracy, which foresaw the use of watch telephones

10. The first microwave ovens were created in which decade?

1950s

Party Round 65

1. What instrument does Kenny G play? (two words)

Soprano saxophone

2. Who was known as The Great Emancipator?

Abraham Lincoln

3. Which of these words is Japanese for uniting or coming together: Toyota, Honda, Nissan, or Subaru?

Subaru

4. The pin stripes were placed on the uniforms of the New York Yankees in 1925 to make which 260-pound player look thinner?

Babe Ruth

5. Name the four main characters of the popular TV comedy series, Seinfeld.

Jerry Seinfeld / Kramer / Elaine / George

6. Mother Theresa, one of the world's most generous people, died September 5, 1997.
a. In which city did she do most of her life's work?
b. Which prestigious award did she win in 1979?
c. Where in 1910 was she born?

Calcutta
Nobel Peace Prize
Yugoslavia or Macedonia to Albanian parents

7. What ancient ritual became a professional sport in Japan in the 1600s?

Sumo Wrestling

8. What did archeologist Howard Carter discover in 1922 near the town of Luxor, Egypt?

King Tut's tomb

9. What two U.S. states, whose names begin with the same letter, are among America's leaders in the production of wheat?

Iowa / Illinois

10. This U.S. city has two professional sports teams whose names are business-related, with opposite meanings. Name the city and the teams.

Chicago Bulls (basketball) / Bears (football))

71

Party Round 66

1. What is sum of the first 50 even numbers, starting with 2?

2550, and the reason is: combine (2+100) + (4+98) + (6+96) = 25 groups of 102

2. The Mafia was formed in the early 19th century, on which island?

Sicily

3. Called the most popular female country singer in history, this glamorous 33-year-old Canadian sold 7 million copies of her 1998 music CD, Come On Over. Who is she?

Shania Twain

4. What's the highest mountain peak in Central Europe, and in what country is it located?

Mt. Blanc / France

5. Authors of classics:
a. Who wrote Don Quixote?
b. The Hunchback of Notre Dame?
c. Twelfth century Persian poem called the Rubáíyát?

Miguel de Cervantes
Victor Hugo
Omar Khayyam

6. In January, 1998, the pope drew large and enthusiastic crowds in his first visit to what Communist country?

Cuba

7. Star Wars creator George Lucas studied film at what university?

University of Southern California

8. What is the psychological name for the group of psychotic disorders marked by withdrawal from reality, delusions, and hallucinations?

Schizophrenia

9. Who was the first U.S. President to be impeached?

Andrew Johnson, impeached by the House in 1868, eventually acquitted by one vote in the Senate

10. Which large musical instrument is named after a composer?

Sousaphone

Party Round 67

1. What is a male donkey called?

Jackass

2. Which mythological figure flew too close to the sun, causing a fall to Earth when the wax in his wings melted?

Icarus

3. Which athlete's 1975 autobiography was titled The Greatest?

Mohammad Ali

4. During the Mexican War of 1846, U.S. forces captured what city along the Pacific known as Yerba Buena (good herb)?

San Francisco

5. What is a 10-letter adjective that describes the brilliant, colorful rainbow-like effect seen in an oil slick?

Iridescent

6. European foods:
a. What's the Italian name for ice cream?
b. What's the French name for a pastry shop (not merely a bakery)?
c. What's the Italian name for spaghetti with meat and tomato sauce?

Gelato
Patisserie

Bolognese

7. One of the most popular events for car racing fans is abbreviated NASCAR. What does that stand for?

National Association for Stock Car Auto Racing

8. Medieval scientists used what form of magic and primitive chemistry to change one chemical element into another, as lead into gold?

Alchemy

9. Enthusiastic, original, audacious musical group, The Rolling Stones, achieved their first #1 hits: July, 1964 in England, and June, 1965, in the U.S. Name the song titles.

England: It's All Over Now / U.S.: I Can't Get No Satisfaction

10. In ancient Rome a special factory was established and dedicated to the Roman God Juno Moneta. What did that factory produce?

Money - derived from the Latin moneta, and such a factory is called a mint

Party Round 68

1. What is the opening title of every Star Wars film?

"Long ago, in a galaxy far, far away..."

2. Jesus Christ most likely spoke what ancient Middle-East language?

Aramaic

3. Certain American Indians used strings of beads made from polished shells as currency, jewelry, or for ceremonial exchanges between groups. What did they call this?

Wampum

4. Which 1999 motion picture, starring Hugh Grant and Julia Roberts, was the first British film ever to earn more than $100 million at the U.S. box office?

Notting Hill

5. 80% of the world's rubber is produced in what three countries?

Thailand / Indonesia / Malaysia

6. What was the first athletic event held in the first Olympic games in 776 B.C.?

Foot race ... Male racers running in the nude

7. Florida was acquired by the U.S.A. in 1819, during the term of office of the shortest president, whose height was 5'2". What was his name?

James Madison

8. Who was the founder of the Buddhist religion?

Siddhartha Gautama, born 563 B.C.

9. What are the three Baltic states?

Estonia / Latvia / Lithuania

10. World War II British air force soldiers named their inflatable life preservers after what sultry, curvaceous American actress?

Mae West

Party Round 69

1. The name of what handy item comes from two Greek words meaning "sound" and "from afar"?

Telephone

2. One of the most popular toys of all time is a plastic ring with a Hawaiian name. What is it?

Hula hoop

3. What was America's first national park, established in 1872?

Yellowstone

4. Which actors played the lead roles in these films with a one-word title:
a. 1976: Rocky
b. 1982: Gandhi
c. 1984: Amadeus

Silvester Stallone
Ben Kingsley
Tom Hulce

5. Her name was Anna Mary Robertson. She took up painting at the age of 76 and continued until her death at age 101. By what name is she better known?

Grandma Moses

6. Besides Michael, who were the other four members of the Jackson Five?

Jackie / Tito / Jermaine / Marlon

7. Who said, in 1965, "Every Communist must grasp the truth: Political power grows out of the barrel of a gun"?

Chinese Communist Leader Mao Zedong

8. The card game now known as bridge was popularized in 1742 by which British games writer?

Edmond Hoyle

9. Cooking conversions: How many tablespoons are in a cup: 16, 32, or 48?

16

10. Which small island nation is a world leader in Internet connections per capita, chess grandmasters, and belief in elves, dwarfs, and trolls?

Iceland

Party Round 70

1. I'll give the common name for heavenly events, you give the scientific name. For example, if I say "the Ram," you would say "Aries."
a. Constellation The Archer
b. Constellation Great Bear
c. Natural Wonder called the Northern Lights

Sagittarius
Ursa Major
Aurora borealis

2. What Holy Roman emperor and 14th century king of Bohemia is frequently mentioned in a Christmas song?

King Wenceslaus

3. Since Queen Elizabeth took the throne, how many U.S Presidents have there been?

10 = Eisenhower / Kennedy / Johnson / Nixon / Ford / Carter / Reagan / Bush / Clinton / Bush (data 2002)

4. In the tales of King Arthur, this young knight had such purity and virtue that he could see the Holy Grail, while other knights could not. Who was he?

Sir Galahad

5. What three actors starred in the 1969 film (and now cult classic) Easy Rider?

Peter Fonda / Dennis Hopper / Jack Nicholson

6. What did Philadelphia Warrior Wilt Chamberlain do in March 1962 that never happened again in an NBA game?

Scored 100 points in a game

7. September 1, 1939, is generally considered the start of World War II, when Germany attacked what country?

Poland

8. Before 1854, the tallest buildings were only 6 floors high. What 1854 invention paved the way for the construction of skyscrapers of almost unlimited height?

The elevator

9. What yellow product was introduced in the 1890s by the Koh-I-Noor Company?

Pencil

10. What is the world's northernmost national capital city?

Reyjkjavik, Iceland

Party Round 71

1. Which brand of television is named for the highest point attained by a celestial body?

Zenith

2. In the world of journalism, The Five Fs is a nickname for the five subjects most commonly found in women's magazines. What are these five Fs?

Food / Fashion / Family / Furnishings / Fitness

3. The loser in the 1962 California election for governor went on to become president of the United States. Who was he?

Richard Nixon

4. Which political leader codified the civil laws of France and most French speaking nations?

Napoleon- the Napoleonic Code

5. The world's oldest film festival is held annually in a European city. What festival is this?

Venice Film Festival

6. These are phrases with animal names:
a. An undesirable family member
b. Baseball star Lou Gehrig
c. Pilot Charles Lindbergh

Black sheep
The Iron Horse
The Lone Eagle

7. Can you name two Oliver Stone films with a Vietnam War theme?

Platoon / Born on the Fourth of July

8. Due to their premature deaths, who were the only two baseball players inducted into the Baseball Hall of Fame before the normal five year waiting period?

Lou Gehrig / Roberto Clemente

9. In what state did the United States test the atomic bomb?

New Mexico

10. How many seconds faster can a car drive one mile at 50 mph than at 40 mph?

18 seconds (at 40 mph: 90 sec.; at 50 mph: 72 sec.)

Party Round 72

1. Three film students set out into the Black Hills to make a documentary about a local witch, in what 1999 film?

The Blair Witch Project

2. People who suffer from myopia can not very well do what?

See distant objects

3. By order of Joseph Stalin, which Russian revolutionary was assassinated while in exile in Mexico in 1940?

Leon Trotsky

4. At the time of the winter solstice that occurs around December 22, the sun is directly overhead the Tropic of what?

Tropic of Capricorn (due to the Earth's tilt)

5. Name the first musical group installed in the Rock and Roll Hall of Fame whose name begins with the letter M.

Mamas and the Papas

6. This South American capital city name means mountain view. Name the city and country.

Montevideo, Uruguay

7. Which two U.S. states were named for the same Sioux Indian tribe?

North / South Dakota

8. The Nobel Prize is given in six fields. Three of them are Peace, Physics, and Chemistry. Name three others.

Any three of...
literature / economics / medicine / physiology

9. In 1984 & 1988: Katarina Witt won the Olympic Gold medal in figure skating. Which country did she represent?

East Germany (but not Germany)

10. Find the total of these three quantities: The number of blackbirds baked in the King's pie, increased by the number of years that Rip Van Winkle slept, diminished by Jack Benny's perennial age?

5 (24 + 20 - 39)

Party Round 73

1. What is the title of Michael Jackson's 1982 mega hit album, one of the largest selling albums of all time, and who produced the album for Michael?

Thriller / Quincy Jones

2. What British monarch died in 1901 at the age of 81?

Queen Victoria

3. What is the name for the meat of young sheep, and what is the name for the meat of fully grown sheep?

Lamb / Mutton

4. What are the most common last names (family names) in each of these countries?
a. Great Britain
b. China
c. Sweden

Smith
Chang
Johansson

5. What European capital city is named for the Trojan prince who abducted Helen of Troy, causing the Trojan War?

Paris

6. Tradition has it that Rome was founded by which twin brothers?

Romulus and Remus

7. What unusual act does a female black widow spider perform after mating?

Eats her mate

8. After the queen of Crete mated with a sacred bull, she gave birth to a monster, half man and half bull, called what?

Minotaur

9. Name these things that are high:
a. The highest hand in poker
b. The highest state of consciousness in Buddhism
c. The highest body in the Judicial branch of our government

Royal Flush
Nirvana
Supreme Court

10. Which breed of spotted dog is named after the region of Yugoslavia where it originated?

Dalmatian

Party Round 74

1. The Byzantine Empire, the eastern portion of the Roman Empire, existed from about 330 A.D. until about 1453 A.D. What was the capital city?

Constantinople, founded by Roman Emperor Constantine the Great

2. What South American ballroom dance swept the world in the early twentieth century?

Tango

3. Baseball's first World Series was played in what year ending with 3?

1903

4. What are the two leading U.S. newspapers in terms of daily circulation?

Wall Street Journal / USA Today

5. What nation borders Russia and China and no other country?

Mongolia

6. Medieval paintings from the Renaissance period frequently depict God sitting on a throne supported by chubby baby angels with wings, called what?

Cherubim or Cherubs. hence, a person with a chubby, childlike face may be called cherubic

7. In 1970, Dr. David Reuben published what popular guide to adult relations with a long catchy title?

Everything You Always Wanted to Know About Sex But Were Afraid to Ask

8. What rhythm-and-blues recording star was shot to death in 1984 by his father after a violent argument?

Marvin Gaye

9. What woman said, "One minute I was a nobody; the next minute I was the Princess of Wales"?

Diana Spencer

10. Davy Jones's Locker is the slang term for what?

Bottom of the ocean

Party Round 75

1. Things that are high:
a. The highest-pitched instrument in the string section of an orchestra — Violin
b. Highest mountain in Africa — Mt. Kilimanjaro
c. The highest military decoration in the United States armed services — Congressional Medal of Honor

2. What actress starred in the films The Big Chill, Fatal Attraction, and 101 Dalmatians? — Glenn Close

3. Give the scientific names for each of the following body parts:
a. Breast bone — Sternum
b. Knee cap — Patella
c. Jaw bone — Mandible

4a. The running of the Bulls occurs every year in what Spanish city? — Pamplona
b. This annual event was celebrated in what 1926 novel by Hemingway? — The Sun Also Rises

5. What 1981 sports film with a hot title won the Academy Award as Best Picture? — Chariots of Fire

6. An 8" by 10" photo is surrounded by a picture frame that is 2" wide. What is the area of the picture frame alone? — 88 sq. inches

7. Can you list the first three of the world's countries in alphabetical order? — Afghanistan / Albania / Algeria

8. Who were the parents of King Solomon? — David / Bathsheba

9. In what year did Disneyland open in Anaheim, California? — 1955

10. Words and names beginning with F:
a. A bad service in tennis — Fault
b. American author of the novel The Sound and the Fury in 1929 — William Faulkner
c. Daughter of the Islamic prophet Muhammad — Fatima

Party Round 76

1. Phrases with numbers in them:
a. Exchanging slaps with upraised palms

b. All the oceans of the world
c. The latest possible time

2. Based on the order in which the Constitution was ratified, what was the first U.S. state?

3. What planet takes about 225 days to orbit the sun?

4. Which nineteenth century English financier established scholarships to train potential leaders at Oxford University?

5. Which two events make up the winter biathlon?

6. Why was a 1969 record album by John and Yoko Ono Lennon sold in a brown paper bag?

7. Name the Academy Award Winning actress for each of thiese films:
a. 1989: Driving Miss Daisy
b. 1939: Gone with the Wind
c. 1960: Butterfield 8

8. Which two women were married to Ronald Reagan?

9. Which small explosive device has a fruity name?

10. What is the area of a square whose diagonal is 10 inches long?

High Five or Give Me Five
Seven Seas
Eleventh Hour

Delaware, followed by Pennsylvania / New Jersey

Venus

Cecil Rhodes, who established the Rhodes Scholarship

Cross Country Skiing / Rifle Marksmanship

They were nude on the cover

Jessica Tandy
Vivien Leigh
Elizabeth Taylor

Jane Wyman / Nancy Davis

Cherry bomb

50 square inches

Party Round 77

1. Which land animal has the longest gestation period, 650 days?

Elephant

2. Figaro is the hero of what Rossini opera?

The Barber of Seville

3. By the end of the 20th century, what was America's fastest growing major city, with a 75% growth rate during the 1990s?

Las Vegas, which grew from 800,000 to 1.4 million during the 1990s

4. These literary authors produced works with numbers in the titles. Name the titles of the author:
a. George Orwell
b. Joseph Heller
c. Kurt Vonnegut

1984
Catch 22
Slaughterhouse 5

5. The first organized game of ice hockey was played in 1879 in what French speaking city?

Montreal

6. The Egyptian queen Cleopatra, who lived in the first century B.C., was famous for her beauty, charm, and luxurious living.
a. She lived for some time in Rome with what Roman leader?
b. After the death of this person she lived in Egypt with what Roman politician?

Julius Caesar

Mark Anthony

7. Name the acting pairs who starred in each of these films:
a. Thomas Crown Affair, 1968

b. The Thomas Crown Affair, 1999

Steve McQueen / Faye Dunaway
Rene Russo / Pierce Brosnan

8. Which European city is named for the Greek goddess of wisdom?

Athens, named for Athena

9. In 1980 a flammable drug mixture used to freebase cocaine exploded, burning the face of what comedian?

Richard Pryor

10. What hereditary blood disease occurs most frequently in people of African descent?

Sickle cell anemia

Party Round 78

1a. The first lunar landing by humans was achieved on July 20, 1969, by astronauts on Apollo flight number what?

11

b. Who was the first man to set foot on the moon?

Neil Armstrong

2. This word can be an infuriating verb or an aromatic noun. What is it?

Incense

3. What two animals are pictured on the Australian Coat of Arms?

Kangaroo / Emu, a flightless bird

4. Name these oldests:

a. The oldest man mentioned in the Bible

Methuselah

b. The oldest person ever elected President of the U.S.A. (age 73 in 1984)

Ronald Reagan

c. Widely regarded as the world's oldest city, still a thriving city today

Damascus, Syria

d. Oldest city in the United States

St. Augustine, Florida

5. What is the hardest substance in the human body and of what chemical element is it composed?

Tooth Enamel / Calcium

6. What winter team sport was first played by female teams for Olympic medals at the 1998 Winter Olympics in Nagano, Japan?

Ice Hockey

7. The selling price of what financial instruments, auctioned each week by the Treasury Department, determines our short term interest rates?

Treasury bills or bonds

8. What cultural rebirth, whose name means revival or rediscovery, occurred in Europe from the fourteenth through the seventeenth centuries?

Renaissance

9. What is the world's most common source of fuel today?

Natural Gas

10. The Houston Comets play the New York Liberty in what sports league?

Women's National Basketball Association

Party Round 79

1. What convict died from a liver disease while serving a 99-year sentence for the assassination of Rev. Martin Luther King?

James Earl Ray

2. What are the three most populous cities that lie within 50 miles of the U.S.-Canada border (in either country)?

Toronto / Montreal / Detroit

3. This bitter substance is scraped from the bark of cinchona trees in the Andes. Doctors use it to treat malaria, and some adults drink it mixed with alcohol. What is it?

Quinine

4. If a 6 1/2 foot-long ladder leans against a building, reaching 6 feet up the building, how far is the base of the ladder from the base of the building?

2 1/2 feet, using the Pythagorean theorem

5. What city was capital of the ancient empire of Babylonia?

Babylon

6. What sad event occurred on April 14, 1912?

The sinking of the unsinkable Titanic

7. The naval officer in charge of a ship's rigging, anchors, cables, and deck crew is called bos'n. How is that word spelled properly?

Botswain

8. In 1974, Barbra Streisand offered Elvis Presley the opportunity to co-star with her in a certain movie, but on Elvis's rejection, Kris Kristofferson eventually got the part. What film was it?

A Star Is Born

9a. In Presidential elections, what winning candidate amassed the largest number of popular votes ever, 54 million?

Ronald Reagan, 1984

b. Since 1950, which U.S. President was elected with the fewest popular votes, only 32 million?

Richard Nixon, 1968

10. Madonna's greatest release of 1996 was a baby daughter with what first name?

Lourdes

Party Round 80

1. Oceanographers agree that the greatest tidal range, the difference between high and low tide levels, occurs under what astronomical conditions?

When the sun and moon are aligned - fall or spring tide

2. You might have in your home what item that pandas eat every day to survive?

Bamboo

3. The most expensive musical instrument ever sold at an auction was sold for $1.6 million at a 1990 auction in London. What type of instrument was it?

Stradivarius Violin

4. In 1974 Elton John had a #1 musical hit with a Beatles song that contains a person's name in the title. What was it?

Lucy In The Sky With Diamonds

5. Name these NBA team locations:
a. Before the Golden State Warriors moved to Oakland in 1971, they were located in what two cities?
b. Before the Utah Jazz moved to Salt Lake City in 1979, they were situated from 1974-1979 in which city?
c. Before the Lakers moved to the Los Angeles in 1960, they were located from 1947-1960 in which city?

San Francisco 1962-71 / Philadelphia 1946-62
New Orleans

Minneapolis

6. What were the last names of Romeo and Juliet?

Montague / Capulet

7a. Television's Tonight Show debuted in 1954. Who was the first host?
b. In what year did Johnny Carson pass the reins to Jay Leno?

Steve Allen

1992

8. What is the name of Europe's highest and most active volcano, 11,000 feet?

Mt. Etna

9. Which jazz composer, pianist, and bandleader with a noble nickname composed Mood Indigo and Take the A-Train?

Duke Ellington, (1899-1974) Edward Kennedy Ellington

10. What was the last North American city to host the Winter Olympics in the 20th century?

Calgary, Canada 1988

Party Round 81

1. What does UNICEF stand for?

United Nations International Children's Emergency Fund

2. What sixteenth century Polish scholar argued that Earth moves about the Sun?

Nicolaus Copericus

3. The procedure for creating artificial rain by human intervention is know by what two-word phrase?

Cloud seeding

4. Shopping history: The first store of this type opened in 1930 in Queens, New York and was immediately successful. Today stores of this type can be found in just about every city of the world. What kind of store is it?

Supermarket

5. Which city in Maine is named for a type of large reindeer native to the region?

Caribou, Maine

6. If the value of a share of stock goes up in value 10% one week, and then drops 10% in value the next week, what is the percentage difference, if any, from the original value?

1% Lower. for example: 100 —> 110 —> 99

7. Members of the Church of Jesus Christ of Latter-Day Saints form the majority of residents of which state?

Utah

8. Can you name three stars of TV's Cheers who went on to successful movie careers?

Ted Danson / Shelley Long / Woody Harrelson / Rhea Perlman

9. Supply the last name of each of these people:
a. Military officer and politician Napoleon
b. Artist Rembrandt
c. Singer Madonna

Bonaparte
Van Rijn or Ryn
Ciccone

10. What is the Nepalese word for "home of the snows"?

Himalaya

Party Round 82

1. What animal is studied in each of the following ...ologies:
a. Ornithology
b. Hippology
c. Ichthyology

Birds
Horses
Fish

2. Which clothing accessory for women, worn as early as the 16th century, made getting through a door difficult, and getting into a carriage almost impossible?

Hoop Skirt

3. In his boxing career, Muhammad Ali lost only five fights. Name any four of the boxers who defeated him.

Joe Frazier / Ken Norton / Leon Spinks / Larry Holmes / Trevor Berbick

4. These bitter political opponents, the vice president of the United States, and the former secretary of the treasury, ended their hatred with a duel in 1804. Who killed whom in that duel?

Aaron Burr killed Alexander Hamilton

5. Name the stage musical that featured each of these songs:
a. Maria
b. On the Street Where you Live
c. What Kind of Fool Am I?

West Side Story
My Fair Lady
Stop the World, I Want to Get Off

6. Automobile maker Henry Ford, President Gerald Ford, basketball star Magic Johnson, singers Aretha Franklin and Madonna, all come from what U.S. state?

Michigan

7. The average life expectancy of humans in the year 1000 A.D. was which of the following: 30 years, 35 years, or 40 years?

30

8. Animals with a segmented spinal column are called vertebrates. There are five classes of vertebrates, one of which is mammals. What are the other four?

Amphibians, birds, fish, and reptiles

9. Which military leader lost two-thirds of his army in a disastrous invasion of Russia in 1812?

Napoleon

10. Which computer programming language is named for an Asian island (or a hot beverage)?

Java

Party Round 83

1. What adult beverage is named for a 16th century queen?

Bloody Mary

2. What is the term for a painting applied directly to a wall?

Mural

3. The largest single land purchase in the history of the United States added over 900,000 square miles to the area of this country in 1803. What was it?

Louisiana Purchase

4. From 1891-1893, Liliuokalani was the last... what.. of Hawaii?

Queen

5. Complete these statements made by 19th century American showman Phineas T. Barnum:
a. "There's a sucker born...
b. "Every crowd has...

... every minute"
... a silver lining"

6. What is the world's largest city south of the equator?

San Paolo, Brazil

7. What is an onomatopoeia, and give a simple example.

A word or phrase that imitates the associated sound, for example buzz, murmur, gargle.

8. Folks with animal names:
a. Athlete Eldridge Woods
b. Green Sesame Street host
c. Jazz musician Charlie Parker

Tiger
Kermit the Frog
Bird

9. Which grow faster: our fingernails or toenails?

Fingernails grow .02 inches per week, four times faster than toenails

10. Greek is an official language in Greece and what other country?

Cyprus: Greek and Turkish are both official languages

Party Round 84

1. The human body contains 70,000 miles of what?

Blood vessels

2. True or False: Worker ants are always female?

True

3. This ancient city on the site of present day Istanbul was founded in 660 B.C. by the Greeks. What did they name it?

Byzantium

4. What is the Japanese word for a woman trained and paid to provide entertainment and company for men?

Geisha

5. Which South American blend of jazz and samba means new trend?

Bossa Nova, a blend of jazz and samba

6. Identify four U.S. state capital cities named after Presidents.

Lincoln, NE / Jackson, MS / Madison, WI /Jefferson City, MO

7. What athlete has been called Superman in Shorts?

Michael Jordan

8. Names for female animals? For example, if I said deer, you say ...doe.
a. Dog
b. Sheep
c. Fox

Bitch
Ewe
Vixen

9. Events that occurred in years ending with 9. Name that year.
a. The United Nations declares Israel a sovereign nation.
b. The Concorde aircraft makes its maiden flight.
c. Alexandre Gustave Eiffel's tower is the high point of the Paris World Exhibition.

1949
1969
1889

10. Before bowling became a ten pin affair, how many pins were used in a game of bowling?

9 pins (when authorities banned this game, another pin was added)

Party Round 85

1. What French-born Swiss theologian, in 1533, broke with the Roman Catholic Church and established a Protestant based government in Geneva, Switzerland?

John Calvin, Presbyterian

2. Musical tempos:
a. From the Italian for "cheerful," this means a brisk, lively tempo.

Allegro

b. From the Italian for "walking," this means a steady, moderately slow musical tempo.

Andante

3. The writing styles of the Sumerians, Assyrians, Babylonians, and Persians all evolved from the oldest type of writing known to mankind, dating from about 3000 B.C. What was it?

Cuneiform

4. What Beatles music album is named after a military character?

Sgt. Pepper's Lonely Hearts Club Band

5. A number of brand name products like Coke or Kleenex have turned into everyday terms. Name the following former brand names, now generic terms:
a. Vacuum cleaner
b. Soother of weary bones
c. Container for beverages

Hoover
Jacuzzi
Thermos

6. What plant has the largest seeds?

Coconut

7. In what London theater were many of Shakespeare's great plays performed?

Globe

8. Identify three major league baseball teams named after birds.

Baltimore Orioles / St. Louis Cardinals / Toronto Blue Jays

9. In any room of your home you could find this product invented around 1500 B.C. What is it?

Glass

10. Name the composers, all of whose first names begin with G, of these famous operas.
a. 1935: Porgy and Bess
b. 1875: Carmen
c. 1904: Madame Butterfly

George Gershwin
Georges Bizet
Guacomo Puccini

Party Round 86

1. The age of pyramid building in Egypt began closest to which of these years? 1700 B.C., 2700 B.C., or 3700 B.C.?

2700 B.C.

2. Frequently, couples march to the marriage altar to the sounds of the Bridal Chorus, based on music from what composer, and what opera?

Richard Wagner's Lohengrin

3. Almost all the English monarchs since William the Conqueror have been crowned at what London location?

Westminster Abbey

4. What city is home to each of these universities?
a. University of Colorado
b. Tulane University
c. Vanderbilt University

Boulder, Colorado
New Orleans
Nashville, Tennessee

5. At a one-hour speech, half the people listen to the entire speech, half the rest listen to half the speech, and everybody else sleeps. What is the average listening time, in minutes per person?

37.5 minutes.
If there are 100 people, 50 people listen to 60 minutes (3000 minutes heard) and 25 people listen to 30 minutes (750 minutes heard). 3750 minutes are heard by 100 people for an average of 37.5 minutes per person

6. In 1998, this elderly gay British actor played the role of an elderly gay film director in Hollywood, and received his first nomination for the Academy Award for Best Actor as a result. Name this actor in the film Gods and Monsters.

Ian McKellen

7. Name the most well-known park (public or amusement) in each of these cities:
a. Anaheim, California
b. Copenhagen, Denmark
b. Moscow, Russia

Disneyland
Tivoli Gardens
Gorky Park

8. What was the Roman name for modern-day France?

Gaul or Gallia

9. The name of what American tourist city means "the meadows" in Spanish?

Las Vegas

10. Who is the Greek god of music, medicine, poetry, and the sun?

Apollo

Party Round 87

1. The name of what article worn by children when eating, comes from the Latin for drinking?

Bib, from the Latin, bibere, to drink

2. What sporting event is named for the 490 B.C. military battle in which a messenger, running back to Athens to report victory over the Persians, collapsed and died upon delivering his message?

Marathon. The length of the modern marathon foot race, 26 miles, 385 yards (41.3 kilometers, is based on this legend.

3. What resort town of southern Florida, just north of Miami, has the same name as a district of Los Angeles?

Hollywood

4. Who was the main villain in the stories of Robin Hood?

Sheriff of Nottingham

5. Residents of Rio de Janeiro call themselves after what dance, similar to the samba?

Carioca (a native of Rio is a Carioca).

6. What popular entertainer starred in a television special every Christmas season from 1950 to 1994?

Bob Hope

7. Founded in 1636, what is the oldest college in America?

Harvard

8. Historians agree that this object, primarily used in sporting events today, was invented 50,000 years ago for survival purposes. What is it?

The bow (used with arrow to kill for food)

9. What is the world's largest religion - the one with the most followers?

Christianity (including Catholic) has 2 billion adherents, while Islam has a bit more than 1 billion followers

10. For the last half of his life, Ludwig van Beethoven lived with what physical infirmity?

Deafness; he began to lose his hearing in 1801 and was deaf by 1819

Party Round 88

1. Which automobile manufacturers produce each of these car models:
a. Infinity
b. Lexus
c. Saturn

Nissan
Toyota
General Motors

2. Which period of history preceded the Iron Age?

The Bronze Age

3. What region of the world has the largest ratio of females to males - where women most outnumber men?

Countries of Eastern Europe, as the former U.S.S.R., Latvia, Ukraine, Belarus

4. Galileo used the phrase "light held together by water" to describe what liquid?

Wine

5. Six-letter names, ending with O. Name these actors:
a. First name Marlon
b. First name Robert
c. First name Alan

Brando
DeNiro
Pacino

6. Women have been playing this outdoor sport competitively since 1866. Vassar College, in Poughkeepsie, NY, had the first woman's team. What sport is it: baseball, soccer, or ice hockey?

Baseball

7. On December 10, 1953, the first Playboy magazine was released. Which well-known woman was the first playmate?

Marilyn Monroe

8. What is the lightest kind of wood?

Balsa

9. Name the most populous city in each of these places beginning with V:
a. Venezuela
b. Vermont
c. Vietnam

Caracas
Burlington
Ho Chi Minh City

10. The name of which edible product comes from French words for sour wine?

Vinegar; vin, wine + aigre, sour

Party Round 89

1. In 1988, an international panel concluded that which former president of Austria had covered-up his World War II Nazi history?

Kurt Waldheim

2. What is the French phrase for the policy of minimal governmental regulation of commerce?

Laissez-faire

3. Scientists claim that the temperature can be determined by counting the sounds produced by which insect?

Cricket

4. Considered one of the greatest Latin American poets, he served as a senator in Chile, was Chile's ambassador to France, and was featured in the film, Il Postino (The Postman). Who is he?

Pablo Neruda

5. What 17th century English king commissioned the best-known English translation of the Bible?

James I

6. Who was the Greek goddess of love and beauty?

Aphrodite

7. Throughout the course of history, more statues have been raised to his person than any other. Who is it?

Buddha

8. He made his film acting debut in 1941 and appeared in more than 50 films. He won the 1953 Academy Award as best male supporting actor for his work in a war film. Who was this popular singer?

Frank Sinatra (1915-1998)

9. On September 4, 1882, Thomas Edison demonstrated what new invention in a one-square-mile section of New York City?

Electric street lighting system

10. In which country did each of these sports originate?
a. Bobsled racing, late 19th century
b. Auto racing, 1878
c. Curling, traditionally

Switzerland
France
Scotland

Party Round 90

1. The primary object used in this 20th century game was originally designed to protect animals. What game is it?

Horseshoes

2. What well-known river flows through each of these cities?
a. Washington, D.C.
b. Vienna, Austria
c. Avignon, France

Potomac
Danube or Donau
Rhone

3. Which fourteenth century author of The Canterbury Tales is called the father of English poetry?

Geoffrey Chaucer

4. What idiom that contains the name of a bird means to discuss in a straightforward manner?

To talk turkey

5. What city hosted the 1782 peace discussions that followed the American revolution against the British?

Paris

6. Name the physical affliction associated with each of these composers:
a. Ludwig Van Beethoven
b. Bach and Handel
c. Antonio Scarlatti

Deaf
Blind
Too fat to play cross-handed on the harpsichord

7. In what cities were these films set?
a. 1989, Do the Right Thing

b. 1985, My Beautiful Laundrette
c. 1973, The Exorcist

Brooklyn (New York City)
London
Washington, D.C.

8. The 1958 financial effort to promote trade and cooperation between Belgium, Luxembourg, the Netherlands, France, Italy, and West Germany resulted in what economic union?

Common Market, and later the European Economic Community

9. In 1904, what French sculptor unveiled a bronze sculpture that he called Le Penseur, translating to what in English?

Francois Auguste Rodin / The Thinker

10. The international airport near Tel Aviv is named after Israel's first prime minister. Who was he?

David Ben-Gurion

Party Round 91

1. A typical coffee tree produces how many pounds of coffee each year: 10, 5, or 1? | One pound

2. Which suburb of Chicago is named for a Roman statesman, orator, and philosopher? | Cicero

3. Which one of these book types was not available in William Shakespeare's day - dictionaries of the English language, books of maps, or biographies of famous people? | Dictionaries

4. Can you name five countries outside of Africa containing the letter Z? | Switzerland / New Zealand / Venezuela / Belize / Brazil / Czech Republic

5. If an equal number of pennies, nickels, dimes, quarters, and half-dollars total $182, how many of each coin are there? | 200 of each

6. What Korean type of martial arts was first contested for medals at the 2000 Sydney Olympics? | Tae Kwon Do

7. What term of endearment is named for an insect product? | Honey

8. The largest Roman Catholic cathedral in the U.S. is located on Fifth Avenue in New York City. What is its name? | St. Patrick's Cathedral

9. What is the name of country singer Garth Brooks' 1991 music album that spent 18 weeks at #1 on the Billboard album charts, and sold over 10 million copies? | Ropin' the Wind

10. In the early 20th century, the publisher of the New York World newspaper instituted a series of annual awards for written work. Who was that publisher? | Joseph Pulitzer

Party Round 92

1. The Beatles, in the early 1960s, made their first studio recordings in what country?

Germany

2. What was the capital city of the Byzantine Empire?

Constantinople

3. Who was Marilyn Monroe's last husband?

Playwright Arthur Miller

4. According to Cockney rhyming slang, what is trouble and strife?

A wife

5. What is the subtitle of the 1999 Star Wars film sequel, strangely entitled Star Wars, Episode I?

The Phantom Menace

6. State whether these places lie north or south of the equator.
a. Honolulu
b. Nairobi
c. Singapore

North
South
North

7. From 1936-1951 Joe DiMaggio was considered the best all-around baseball player; he hit safely in 56 consecutive games.
a. What position did Joe play?
b. What were his two famous nicknames?

Center field
Jolting Joe / The Yankee Clipper

8. "Parting is such sweet sorrow" comes from act 2, scene 2, of what Shakespearean play?

Romeo and Juliet

9. Residents of what country lead the world in seeing visions of the Virgin Mary?

Italy

10. Fans visiting Graceland in Memphis, Tennessee can stay in a hotel cleverly named after which of Elvis' musical hits?

Heartbreak Hotel

Party Round 93

1. The first-ever World Cup of Soccer was held in 1930, in a South American country whose capital city name means mountain-view. What country was it?

Uruguay, whose capital is Montivideo

2. A commodity is defined as a transportable article of trade or commerce, especially an agricultural or mining product. What are the two largest selling commodities in the world?

Oil / Coffee

3. The second wife of King Henry VIII, and the mother of Queen Elizabeth I, she was convicted of adultery and beheaded. Who was she?

Anne Boleyn

4. Which U.S. capital city was a major center of agitation against England in the 18th century, and a leading anti-slavery stronghold in the 19th century?

Boston

5. Today you can buy this handy small item for less than $1, but when Hungarian Laszlo Biro invented it in 1938, it was a revolutionary advance in the field of communication, and cost $12.50. What is it?

Ball point pen

6. Name the capital city of each of these countries:
a. Canada
b. Indonesia
c. Serbia

Ottawa
Djakarta
Belgrade

7. To avenge the persecution of Roman Catholics in England, Guy Fawkes was executed for his role in the November 5, 1605 Gunpowder Plot, an attempt to kill what king, and blow up what building?

James I / Parliament. Guy Fawkes Day is recalled annually on November 5

8. The edible animal called "humu humu nuku nuku apua'a" is the state...what ... of Hawaii?

Fish

9. America's first postage stamp featuring a living person was issued in June 1927, to honor someone's great achievement one month earlier. Who was featured on that stamp?

Charles Lindbergh, to honor the first solo trans-Atlantic flight, in the plane Spirit of St. Louis

10. What occupation was portrayed in various television shows by actors Bill Cosby, Robert Vaughn, Diana Rigg, and Don Adams?

Spy

Party Round 94

1. Name the authors of each of these classics of literature.
a. Dracula
b. Frankenstein
c. Tarzan

Bram Stoker
Mary Shelley
Edgar Rice Burroughs

2. Give these foreign phrases:
a. The feeling of having experienced something before, in French
b. The other way around, in Latin
c. To your good health, in German

Deja vu

Vice versa
Gesundheit

3. Identify three major league baseball teams that have played most frequently in the World Series (give the team names regardless of cities).

Accept any three:
Yankees / Dodgers / Giants / Cardinals

4. If you draw a five-pointed star, what is the sum of the degree measures of the five angles, located one at each point?

360 degrees

5. Name any three of Michelangelo's most famous works of art or sculpture.

David / the Pieta / Sistine Chapel / Dome of Saint Peter's Basilica / plans for Saint Peter's Church

6. Her career began as a model in the 1930s; she rose from bit player to star, acting in dozens of Hollywood films, on Broadway and television. Who was she?

Lucille Ball

7. What military leader conquered India in 327 B.C.?

Alexander the Great

8. Which pharmaceutical company produced each of these popular products?
a. Viagra
b. Prozac

Pfizer
Lilly

9. What Spanish city lies along the Mediterranean Sea in northwest Africa, totally surrounded by Morocco?

Ceuta

10. Almond-flavored Italian liqueur is known by what name?

Amaretto

Party Round 95

1. The name of what water vehicle can be spelled the same backward and forward?

Kayak

2. Name any three teams that have most frequently won the European Cup of soccer football, contested annually since 1955 by various national champions.

Real Madrid / AC Milan / Ajax Amsterdam / Liverpool

3. The hottest teen music idols of the early 1990s was a boy-band with what child-like name?

New Kids on the Block

4. The Declaration of Independence (1776), Articles of Confederation (1781), and U.S. Constitution (1787) were all adopted in what building?

Independence Hall, in Philadelphia, Pennsylvania

5. In the first line of the John Keats poem Endymion, what four words precede the line, ... "is a joy forever?"

A thing of beauty

6. In June 1963, 26-year-old Valentina Tereshkova became the first woman ever to do this, and she did it 48 times. What was it?

She orbited Earth (aboard Vostok 6)

7. What acting family included John, Ethel, Lionel and Drew?

Barrymore

8. On which stock market are each of these companies listed:
a. McDonald's

New York Stock Exchange

b. Microsoft
c. Phillips Electronics

NASDAQ
Amsterdam

9. Which young, curious artist learned about human anatomy by studying dissected corpses at the hospital of Santa Spiritu in Florence in 1492?

Michelangelo Buonarroti

10. What high-tech company in the 1970s developed the computer concept of clicking a mouse and moving graphical icons to open and store programs?

Xerox (but they dropped the idea, allowing Apple Computers to adapt it to the Macintosh)

Party Round 96

1. The symbol for males, a circle supporting a diagonal arrow, and for females, a circle above a cross, are zodiac signs for which planets?

Male: Mars
Female: Venus

2. At which bodies of water do you find these bridges:
a. Key Bridge connecting Georgetown and Arlington, Virginia?

Potomac River

b. That very old covered bridge decorated with paintings in Lucerne, Switzerland?

Lake Lucerne

c. London Bridge?

Lake Havasu, Arizona

3. The description, "A wolf in sheep's clothing," refers to a ruthless person in an innocent disguise, and comes from which of these sources: The Old Testament, Jesus, or William Shakespeare?

Jesus

4. Which grayish European bird with a well-known two-note call lays its eggs in the nests of other birds?

Cuckoo

5. Meryl Streep won the Oscar in 1979 and 1982 for her roles in what films?

Sophie's Choice / Kramer vs. Kramer

6. The 1926 novel, The Murder of Roger Ackroyd, is considered one of the best murder mysteries ever written. Who wrote it?

Agatha Christie

7. William Shakespeare was born and died on the same month and date. When was it?

Born April 23, 1564 / died April 23, 1616

8. What former student of the Massachusetts Institute of Technology later became prime minister of Israel?

Benjamin Netanyah

9. How are model ships placed in bottles?

Constructed first, body laid in bottle, masts lowered, then masts rise up in the bottle

10. What professional basketball player was voted the NBA's most valuable player 1984-86, as well as coach of the year in 1998, and for what teams?

Larry Bird / played with Boston Celtics / coached the Indiana Pacers

Party Round 97

1. Where in Asia are each of these international airports located?
a. Indira Gandhi Int'l Airport
b. Chiang Kai-Shek Int'l Airport
c. Narita Int'l Airport

New Delhi, India
Taipei, Taiwan
Tokyo

2. What building material is composed of limestone and clay mixed with water?

Cement

3. What are the two most populous counties in the United States?

Los Angeles County / Cook County, (home of Chicago, Illinois

4. In 1998 competing movie studios Dreamworks and Disney/Pixar released similar animated films about insects. What were the film titles?

Antz (Dreamworks) / A Bug's Life (Pixar / Disney)

5. Identify the modern names for each of these countries:
a. Siam
b. Ceylon
c. Abyssinia

Thailand
Sri Lanka
Ethiopia

6. When Gina runs 100 meters in 10 seconds, she is moving at how many kilometers per hour?

36 km/hr

7. The beloved poem, The Night Before Christmas, was written in 1823 by which American scholar and poet?

Clement Clarke Moore (1779-1863) (the original title was A Visit from St. Nicholas)

8. A school in Reigate, England recently changed its name to The Orchard School, because of a certain offensive TV show. What was the previous name of the school?

South Park

9. Phrases containing the word dog:
a. A frankfurter covered with meat, beans, and peppers
b. Ruthlessly competitive
c. One who guards or protects against waste or illegal practices

Chili dog
Dog eat dog
Watchdog

10. Her many supporters called her the Empress of India. She died on January 22, 1901 at the age of 82. Who was she?

Queen Victoria

Party Round 98

1. Thirty-six years after being the first American to orbit the Earth, what 77-year old former senator returned to space in October 1998?

John Glenn

2. What's the proper name for a badminton birdie?

Shuttlecock

3. Food shopping was simplified after the 1937 invention of what metal product?

Shopping cart

4. The Murray River rises in this country's Alp-like mountains, then flows about 2,600 km (1,600 miles) into the Indian Ocean. What country is it in?

Australia (it flows into the Indian Ocean south of Adelaide)

5. What number comes next: 2,5,10,17,26,?

37

6. What team won the championship of the Woman's National Basketball Association each of its first four years of existence, beginning in 1996?

Houston Comets

7. Which U.S. President won the Nobel Peace Prize in 1906 for negotiating an end to the Russo-Japanese War of 1904?

Theodore Roosevelt

8. The fastest fish is speedier than the fastest land animal. It can move through the water at almost 70 mph. What kind of fish is it?

Sailfish

9. Name two countries that were allies with the U.S. and Britain in World War I, but enemies in World War II.

Primarily Italy and Japan / also Romania and Thailand

10. Which Irish-born novelist and playwright, whose plays include Waiting for Godot (1952), won the 1969 Nobel Prize for literature?

Samuel Beckett

Party Round 99

1. Things that are last:
a. The last teeth to erupt
b. The last political leader of the U.S.S.R.

Wisdom Teeth
Mikhail Gorbachev (he won the 1990 Nobel Peace Prize)

2. What television comedy achieved its highest ratings ever for its May 2, 1997 broadcast, when the lead star came out of her gay closet?

Ellen, starring Ellen Degeneres

3. The largest former Soviet Republic is Russia. What is second largest in area?

Kazakhstan

4. Our modern banking system traces its development to the 13th-17th century in what European country?

Italy (Banco = bench. Bankers worked on benches in the street)

5. Name the the four children of Queen Elizabeth II and Prince Phillip.

Charles / Anne / Andrew / Edward

6. Before clocks were invented, people could determine the proper time by a number of mechanical methods. Name three.

Sundials / Water Clocks / Church Bells / Candles / ...

7. Presidents John F. Kennedy and Bill Clinton have seven, Ronald Reagan and Jimmy Carter have six, and George Bush and Gerald Ford only have only four of what?

Letters in last name

8. In 1984, as singer Michael Jackson was earning $1.5 million dollars filming a Pepsi commercial, he had a life-threatening accident. What happened?

Hair caught fire

9. Name the northernmost and southernmost cities of North America that have major league baseball teams.

Seattle Mariners (more northerly even than any Canadian teams)/ Miami (Florida Marlins)

10. Who is the best selling Dutch writer of all time?

Anne Frank (her diary sold more copies world-wide than any other Dutch writer)

Party Round 100

1. What state in the eastern United States is large enough to swallow up five of its closest neighboring states?

Maine's area could absorb the remaining states of New England

2. What large musical instrument, fitted with steam whistles and played from a keyboard, is most frequently associated with circus parades?

Calliope, named for the muse of epic poetry (from Greek kallos, beauty)

3. What are the three most highly populated countries in Africa?

Nigeria / Egypt / Ethiopia

4. Which comedy actress and TV personality played the role of Miss Hannigan in the film, Annie?

Carol Burnett

5. Which well-known person, of very mysterious and spiritual nature, died on Halloween, October 31, 1926?

Harry Houdini

6. Between 12 noon and 12 midnight, how many times do the hands of a clock form a 900° angle?

23 times; between 5:00 and 7:00 p.m. one right angle is lost

7. What hockey player holds the record for most goals scored in Stanley Cup playoff games?

Wayne Gretzky (122 in a 16 year career)

8. Plastic was invented in 1907, partly as a substitute for what natural material that was in short supply?

Ivory

9. The largest Christian church building in the world is located in Vatican City. What is it?

St. Peter's Basilica

10. What U.S. navy battleship, named after a state, was sunk by the Japanese at Pearl Harbor on December 7, 1941?

U.S.S. Arizona

Trivia for Travelers

Trivia for Travelers
Trivia for Travelers Round 1

1. The Amazon River meets the Pacific Ocean in what country?

Brazil

2. In Earth's southern hemisphere, which two months contain winter and no other seasons?

July / August

3. What is the only coffee grown and produced in the United States?

Kona

4. Which well-loved athlete lit the flame inaugurating the Olympic Games in Atlanta on July 19, 1996?

Muhammad Ali

5. What capital city lies on the Tigris River?

Baghdad, Iraq

6. Two of the world's finest universities: one in England, one in the U.S.A., are located in towns with the same name. Can you identify these two schools?

The city is Cambridge: Cambridge University In England / Harvard University in Massachusetts

7. The world's highest waterfall, 980 mi. (3,200 ft.) high, has what heavenly name, and is located in which country?

Angel Falls / Venezuela

8. Although sober, reliable, unthreatening, and holding a valid airline ticket, what category of passengers may legally be denied an airline seat?

Pregnant women

9. In 1989, this European monarchy with 5 million inhabitants was the world's first nation to legalize gay marriages. Which country is it?

Denmark

10. What is the highest mountain peak in North America?

Mt. McKinley, Alaska

Trivia for Travelers Round 2

1. The Hindu Kush mountain range runs for 500 miles, westward from Pakistan to what country?

Afghanistan

2. The carioca is a dance similar to the samba; the fun loving citizens of what southern city call themselves cariocas?

Rio de Janeiro, Brazil

3. What is the largest lake in central Europe?

Lake Geneva/ Genfersee / Lac Leman

4. Can you name three Italian cheeses that begin with the letter P?

Parmesan / Provolone / Pecorino

5. This African country, settled by returning black slaves, speaks English, uses the dollar for currency, and has a capital city named for a U.S. President. Name the country and the capital.

Liberia / Monrovia

6. Food names in different languages:
a. French fries in British
b. Eggplant in French
c. Smoked salmon in Yiddish

Chips
Aubergine
Lox

7. Travelers in Milano, Italy, can visit one of the leading opera houses of the world, called what?

La Scala

8. The tallest man-made structure in the world stands in which of these places: Chicago, Russia, Malaysia, or North Dakota?

North Dakota - Television Tower - 2064 feet (625 meters)

9. Which country of Africa extends farthest north?

Tunisia

10. Name the most populous city in each of these places:
a. The country of Vietnam

Ho Chi Minh City, formerly Saigon

b. The Canadian province of British Columbia
c. The U.S. state of Nebraska

Vancouver
Omaha

Trivia for Travelers Round 3

1. The Wright brothers first flew a plane in 1903 in what North Carolina location?

Kitty Hawk

2. What small southern California city along the Pacific coastline has been victim of floods, mudslides, earthquake, and wildfires?

Malibu, just west of Los Angeles

3. In 1890, he and his brother organized the American Tobacco Company, and with their wealth they endowed Trinity College of North Carolina. What was their family name?

Duke - Benjamin and James. Trinity College was renamed Duke University in their honor (1924).

4. Name these phrases containing 7:
a. The Pyramids and Hanging Gardens of Babylon are two of them
b. Abbie Hoffman, Jerry Rubin, Dave Dellinger were three of them

Seven Wonders of the World
Chicago Seven (who tried to upset the 1968 Republican Presidential Convention)

c. Capitoline is the highest of them

Seven Hills of Ancient Rome

5. Since the early 1700s nearly all British prime ministers have lived at what London street address?

Number 10 Downing Street

6. In China these noodle-dough dumplings, filled with meat and boiled in soup, are called what?

Won ton

7. What Los Angeles suburb is named for the Roman goddess of fruit and fruit trees: Pomona, Glendora, or Pasadena?

Pomona

8. Identify these names beginning with L:
a. The state containing New Orleans
b. A Tibetan Buddhist monk
c. The most famous tax-protesting English noblewoman of Coventry, England

Louisiana
Lama
Lady Godiva

9. What highly visible mountain in Phoenix, Arizona is named for a desert animal?

Camelback Mountain

10. Identify the currency used in these nations:
a. Netherlands
b. South Africa
c. Israel

Guilder
Rand
Shekel

Trivia for Travelers Round 4

1. The East Side of New York City refers to those Manhattan streets east of what numbered avenue?

Fifth Avenue

2. The church of Santa Maria delle Grazie in Milano houses a fresco of what famous painting, created by whom?

The Last Supper / Leonardo Da Vinci

3. Name the capital city of each of these places:
a. South Carolina
b. The former East Germany
c. North Korea

Columbia
East Berlin
Pyongyang

4. I'll give the old name for the country, you supply the modern name:
a. Siam
b. Abyssinia
c. Southern Rhodesia

Thailand
Ethiopia
Zimbabwe

5. Words beginning with K:
a. Your fate or destiny, according to Hinduism and Buddhism?
b. Disputed region of northern India and Pakistan
c. A cloth headdress worn by Arabic men

Karma

Kashmir
Kaffiyeh

6. What three countries are known as the Baltic States?

Estonia / Latvia / Lithuania

7. One of the ancient wonders of the world is a 105-foot tall bronze statue of Helios (Apollo) completed in 280 B.C. but destroyed during an earthquake in 224 B.C. Located on an island in Greece, what is this statue?

Colossus of Rhodes

8. Which one of these countries is NOT part of Asia's Golden Triangle - Laos, Cambodia, Thailand, or Burma?

Cambodia

9. The food served before a meal to stimulate the appetite has different names in different languages:
a. In English it has a simple logical name.
b. In French it literally means outside the main work.
c. In Italian it frequently consists of meat, fish, cheese, vegetables.

Appetizer
Hors d'oeuvre
Antipasto

10. At the end of the cold war, many countries of eastern Europe abandoned rigid Communist Party rule. What was the last European country to do so?

Albania

Trivia for Travelers Round 5

1. Name the soft white Greek cheese usually made from goat's milk.

Feta

2. Germany, France, and Switzerland all meet at what Swiss city on the Rhine River?

Basel

3. A certain Asian country's capital city is named for its official religion. Name the city and country.

Islamabad, Pakistan

4. Identify two U.S. state capitals whose names end with the 5-letter Greek word for city?

Indianapolis, Indiana and Annapolis, Maryland

5. In which cities are these universities located?
a. Temple University
b. Rice University
c. Dartmouth College

Philadelphia, PA
Houston, TX
Hanover, NH

6. In 1940 there were about 6 million farms in the U.S. By the year 2000 there were about 2, 6 or 10 million?

2 million

7. What idyllic region of palm trees and beaches, located along the Arabian Sea in southwest India, was formerly occupied by the Portuguese?

Goa

8. Actress and political activist Jane Fonda said, "It was the most horrible thing I could possibly have done. It was thoughtless." What 1972 event was she apologizing for?

Posing for photographs with North Vietnamese soldiers, earning her the nickname Hanoi Jane

9. What two neighboring nations were the world's first to embrace Islam?

Saudi Arabia / Yemen

10. One of the world's great rivers rises in the mountains of Tibet and flows southeastward to the South China Sea in Vietnam. What river is it?

Mekong River

Trivia for Travelers Round 6

1. Many of the plants used to make mustard in factories near Dijon are grown not in France, but in what large country outside of Europe?

Canada - note the French connection

2. About 35 miles wide (56 km) and 135 miles long (220 km), what eastern Mediterranean country gained its independence from France in 1943?

Lebanon

3. Which three cities of the world contain the most Mexicans?

Mexico City / Guadalajara / Los Angeles

4. How many countries share a land border with France?

8: Spain, Italy, Switzerland, Germany, Luxembourg, Belgium, Monaco, Andorra

5. Her name was Elizabeth Cochrane Seaman, and she was a journalist for the New York World newspaper. In 1889 she wrote a news article (with pen name Nellie Bly) describing the 72 days she spent doing what?

Attempting to travel around the world, in a balloon, in less than 80 days

6a. Tourists from all over the world travel to the isolated center of Australia to visit the world's largest single rock mass. What is it?

Uluru / also known as Ayer's Rock

b. What town of about 22,000 population lies only 200 miles away?

Alice Springs, whose local economy benefits from tourism and mining

7. Which island in the Caribbean Sea lies closest to South America?

Trinidad - sighted by Columbus in 1498

8. Besides X, Y, and Z, what three letters do not begin the name of any U.S. state?

B, E, J

9. Which one of these is not the name of a city of Japan: Hitachi, Nikko, Sanyo, Toyota?

Sanyo

10. What is the principal island of French Polynesia, and in what body of water do these islands lie?

Tahiti / South Pacific

Trivia for Travelers Round 7

1. After Sydney and Melbourne, what is the third largest city in Australia?

Brisbane

2. What is the Spanish word for a person of mixed racial ancestry, especially of mixed European and Native American ancestry?

Mestizo

3. French army officer Alfred Dreyfuss and Henri Charriere, author of Papillon, were two of the most famous residents of what penal colony off the coast of French Guiana?

Devil's Island

4. Can you name four resort locations mentioned in the chorus of the Beach Boys song, Kokomo?

Aruba, Jamaica, Bermuda, Bahamas, Key Largo, Montego

5. The first hot in-flight meal was served in 1935 by what airline?

Pan American

6. Canada is composed of ten provinces and three territories, the last of which was created in 1999 and given to the native Inuit peoples to govern. Name the three territories of Canada.

Northwest Territory / Yukon / Nunavut

7. What country lies at the eastern end of the island of Hispaniola in the West Indies?

Dominican Republic

8. What is the Japanese dish of deep fried vegetables and seafood?

Tempura

9. Her name is Vigdis Finnbogadottir, and in 1980, she became the world's first democratically elected female head of state. Which isolated country did she represent?

Iceland

10. Edward Kennedy became engulfed in scandal when he accidentally drove off a bridge with which woman on what island?

Mary Jo Kopechne / Chappaquiddick Island at Cape Cod in Massachusetts

Trivia for Travelers Round 8

1. Born on the island of Lesbos about 600 B.C., she was a lyrical poet who led a circle of young female disciples in study of music and the arts. Who was she?

Sappho (her lyrics celebrate friendship among women, but Sappho valued the company of both men and women, was married, and had a daughter)

2. The Pony Express mail service, established in 1860, could carry mail by horseback 2,000 miles in 10 days. What were the easternmost and westernmost states of this rapid mail service?

Missouri and California (Saint Joseph, Missouri and Sacramento, California)

3. From 1859 to 1869, the Suez Canal was designed, engineered, and constructed by a company from which country?

France

4. The very old university city of Cambridge, England lies on which river: the Stratford, the Oxford, or the Cam?

Cam

5. Formerly known as the exotic Spice Islands, the Moluccas are part of what country: The Philippines, Indonesia, or Malaysia?

Indonesia, settled 16th c. by the Portuguese but taken 17th c. by the Dutch, who monopolized the spice trade

6. Osso buco is an Italian dish consisting primarily of what ingredient?

Braised veal in white wine

7. This Korean form of self defense has existed for 2,000 years, and became a medal sport at the Sydney Olympics in 2000. What is this martial art?

Tae Kwon Do

8. Which island nation is separated into two politically unfriendly sectors, the Greek and the Turkish?

Cyprus, in the eastern Mediterranean

9. The steps of the New York public library are guarded by what animals (in statue form)?

Lions

10. Which European capital city lies closest to Paris?

Brussels

Trivia for Travelers Round 9

1. Which word, meaning confusion and noise, comes from the name of a structure in the Bible?

Babel (after the tower of Babel, and the word babel comes from a Hebrew word meaning noise or confusion)

2. Found on most French coins are three words, the motto of France. What are they?

Liberté / Egalité / Fraternité

3. In the history of ship development, around 3000 B.C., what was the first civilization to discover sails and build boats out of planks of wood?

Egyptians

4a. Around 1200 A.D., which crude band of warriors from the north plundered and occupied China, southern Russia, and Iran?

Mongols

b. Which barbarian, whose name meant universal ruler, was their leader?

Genghis Khan

5. In which ancient country was society divided into four social classes: traders, artisans, farmers, and warriors (listed from lowest to highest)?

Japan

6. Although this river has a short name, it is the longest in Italy, flowing 640 km. (400 miles) from Torino towards Venice. Name this river.

Po River

7. The ecosystem of many rivers of south-east Asia, including the Mekong, have been damaged by what large-scale local industry?

Logging, transporting logs by river

8. Which spicy food additive is named after the capital of French Guyana? (two-word answer)

Cayenne Pepper

9. Residents of which U.S. state got their nickname from the tar seeping out of the local ground?

North Carolina - Tarheels

10. If you take a 2,000 mile automobile trip, and use five tires equally, how many miles is each tire used?

1,600 miles. Why? Because 8,000 miles of tire use is divided among five tires.

116

Trivia for Travelers Round 10

1. In 1497, what Portuguese explorer was the first European to sail to India?

Vasco Da Gama

2. Which word sounds like the name of a city in Michigan, but means skillful and adept under pressure?

Adroit

3. The Scottish folk song "You'll take the high road, and I'll take the low road, and I'll be in Scotland before you" is titled after what body of water?

Loch Lomond..."But me and my true love will never meet again, on the bonnie, bonnie banks of Loch Lomond."

4. The hill near Jerusalem on which Jesus was crucified has two names. What are they?

Calvary / Golgotha

5. The Byzantine Empire reached its greatest extent under this Emperor. Art and architecture flourished during his reign, and he built the magnificent Hagia Sophia in Constantinople. Who is he?

Justinian

6. During the Vietnam War, North Vietnamese forces were able to move soldiers and supplies along the Ho Chi Minh Trail, which skirted the border of Vietnam and what two countries?

Laos / Cambodia

7. For how many years did the Berlin Wall stand? (1 year margin of error)

28 years, 1961-89

8. What 8 letter word has all these in common?
a. A color
b. A type of wine
c. A French region, 15th century European power

Burgundy

9. This writing material, perfected in the 2nd century B.C., was made from the skins of sheep or goats, and surpassed papyrus as the most important writing material in the ancient world. It is still used today for certain documents, for lampshades, and for drum and banjo heads. What is it?

Parchment

10. Which line of fortification along France's eastern border with Germany was designed and named for the 1920s French minister of war? (Considered impregnable, the line was breached and captured by the Nazis)

Maginot Line, proposed by Andre Maginot

Trivia for Travelers Round 11

1. What is Earth's smallest ocean?

Arctic

2. What peninsula is occupied by Spain and Portugal?

Iberian

3. The mid-forehead dot worn by some Hindu women indicates their marital status. What color of dot represents married? Red, white, or black?

Red

4. From the age of 23 until his death at 92, Pablo Picasso lived in what city?

Paris

5. In the film, Beverly Hills Cop, Eddie Murphy played the role of a policeman from which city?

Detroit

6. What is the southernmost country in which a Eurail Pass is valid?

Greece

7. In what city do you find the oldest University in Germany?

Heidelberg

8. In 1876 rubber grew primarily in one country, from which the British took thousands of seedlings and planted them around the world. Which country was this?

Brazil

9. What type of TV newscaster has the same name as the lowest graduating cadet at the U.S. Naval Academy in Annapolis?

Anchor man (or woman)

10. Which independent nation has 30,000 inhabitants in less than one square mile of area, and receives over a million visitors per year?

Monaco

Trivia for Travelers Round 12

1. Name the most populous city in each of these places:
a. Florida
b. China
c. Australia's Victoria state

Jacksonville
Shanghai
Melbourne

2. This region, first explored by Lewis and Clark in 1805, was held jointly by Great Britain and the United States from 1818 to 1846, and became the 43rd U.S. state in 1890. Name this state with a panhandle.

Idaho

3. Identify three Canadian provinces whose names begin with the letter N?

Newfoundland / Nova Scotia / New Brunswick

4. Two of the world's most active volcanoes are located on the big island of Hawaii. Name the volcanoes.

Any two of Mauna Loa, Mauna Kea, or Kilauea

5. After his final loss to Britain at the Battle of Waterloo, Napoleon was exiled to what island in the south Atlantic Ocean?

St. Helena

6. Besides the United Kingdom and United States, identify four countries whose names begin with the letter U.

Uganda / Ukraine / United Arab Emirates / Uruguay / Uzbekistan

7. Tallest mountains:
a. 14,000 foot Mount Elbert is the highest point in which U.S. state?

Colorado

b. 3,200 ft. (980 mi.) Scafell Pike is the highest point in what European country?

England

8. Crossword puzzle clue: capital of a European country, four letters, third letter L. What is it?

Oslo

9. These Indonesian islands were named in the Moluccas in the 16th century by the Portuguese, but 17th century Dutch settlers preferred to call them by what delicious name?

The Spice Islands

10. The world's three most populous countries are China, India, and U.S.A. What three countries follow next?

Indonesia / Brazil / Russia

Trivia for Travelers Round 13

1. When it's 12 noon in New York City, what time is it in Panama?

12 noon, Panama is directly south of the U.S. East Coast

2. What country is composed of exactly three islands: North Island, South Island, and Stewart Island?

New Zealand

3. What is the world's largest city that is located in two continents?

Istanbul - on the border of Europe and Asia

4. Which city of northeast Scotland lies on the North Sea at the mouth of the Dee River?

Aberdeen

5. Which two major train stations in Paris are located about one block apart?

Gare du Nord / Gare de l'Est

6. What type of military knife is named after the town in southwest France where it was first made?

Bayonet, from Bayonne

7. Historically, many main roads have been built by throwing the earth from the side ditches toward the center, thus elevating the road above the surrounding ground. This gives rise to what common word?

Highways

8. When the Romans occupied present day London, what did they call it?

Londinium

9. Shared by Chile and Argentina, what island lies at the southern most tip of South America?

Tierra Del Fuego

10. A ship passing through the Panama canal from Pacific to Atlantic travels in what general direction: northeast, northwest, southeast, or southwest?

Northwest

Trivia for Travelers Round 14

1. Conqueror Genghis Khan's 13th century empire was the world's largest ever. It stretched from China in the east to what European river?

Danube

2. Which country was placed under U.S. sanctions in 1950 and remained that way for the rest of the century?

North Korea

3. Where were they born?
a. Singer Celine Dion - what country?
b. Islamic founder Muhammad - what city?
c. President Abraham Lincoln - what state?
d. Inventor of the telephone, Alexander Graham Bell - what nation?

Canada
Mecca
Kentucky
Scotland

4. Terms with geographical origin:
a. Perfumed liquid made from fragrant oils named for a European city
b. Rigorously self-disciplined or self-restrained, named for an ancient city-state

Cologne

Spartan

5. This region was a religious center devoted to the worship of Zeus and the site of the ancient Olympic games. What was it?

Olympia

6. Israel's airport is named after the country's first prime minister. What is it?

Ben-Gurion Airport, named for David Ben-Gurion

7. What was the first national park in the U.S.A.?

Yellowstone

8. Venice attractions:
a. A beautiful bridge named for the island where a market was situated.
b. The grand piazza and grand cathedral of Venice, named after a holy man.

Rialto

San Marco / St Mark's, begun in 830 A.D.

9. What country is bordered by the Caribbean Sea, Nicaragua, El Salvador, Guatemala, and the Pacific Ocean?

Honduras

10. Capital cities:
a. Charleston is the capital of what U.S. state?
b. Winnipeg is capital of what Canadian province?
c. Asunción is the capital of what South American country?

West Virginia
Manitoba
Paraguay

Trivia for Travelers Round 15

1. In the 19th century this Cape Cod island was the center of the Massachusetts whaling industry. Today it's a popular tourist resort, artist center, and site of a whaling museum. What is it?

Nantucket

2. This cold country is a world leader in per capita use of wireless technology. Over 70 percent of its 5 million residents are armed with cell phones and other wireless tools. What country?

Finland

3. Name the two places on Earth where the Greenwich Meridian meets the International Date Line?

North and South Pole

4. Napoleon Bonaparte's two significant islands:
a. After being forced in 1814 to abdicate as emperor of France, Napoleon was exiled to what island?

Elba

b. However he escaped, briefly regained power, and was later exiled for life to which island?

St. Helena

5. When 16th century Portuguese explorers first noticed the prolific bearded fig trees of what West Indies island, they named it the bearded?

Barbados

6. Greek is officially spoken in two different countries of the world. Greece is one. What's the other?

Cyprus

7. North America's most violent earthquake, measuring 8.3 on the Richter scale, occurred in 1964 in a city that calls itself the largest city in the largest state. Where did this disaster occur?

Anchorage

8. What is the longest river in England?

Thames

9. With about 2.5 million inhabitants, what is the most populous city of the West Indies?

Havana, Cuba

10a. If you rearrange six of the letters in the words United States, you get the name of which U.S. state capital city?

Austin

b. If you rearrange five of the letters, you get the name of which African country?

Sudan

c. If you rearrange five of the letters, you get the name of which mountain range?

Andes

Trivia for Travelers Round 16

1. Name the sea on which each of these cities is located:
a. Beirut, Lebanon
b. Venice, Italy
c. Bombay, India

Mediterranean Sea
Adriatic Sea
Arabian Sea

2. What islands became a territory of the United States in 1900?

Hawaii

3a. The world's longest train line, almost 6,000 miles (9300 km.) in length, connects Moscow and what eastern Russian city?
b. What is this rail line called?

Vladivostok

Trans Siberian Railway

4. What cold region of the Earth is named for the Greek word for bear?

Arctic

5. Much of the world's illicit opium comes from a region known as the Golden Triangle. Which three countries meet to form the Golden Triangle?

Burma / Thailand / Laos

6. Who said, "In the West there is loneliness, which I call the leprosy of the West. In many ways it, is worse than our poor in Calcutta."

Mother Theresa

7. Canada's smallest province is named after what person, father of Queen Victoria?

Prince Edward Island, named after Edward, Duke of Kent

8. Name the rivers:
a. On which the Aswan Dam was built
b. One of the rivers of Hades
c. Part of the title of the 1947 Oscar winning film

Nile
Styx
Bridge Over the River Kwai

9. Name the capital city of each of these countries:
a. Brazil
b. Albania
c. Ethiopia

Brazilia
Tirana
Addis Ababa

10. State songs:
a. The Old Folks at Home by Stephen Foster, (Way down upon the Swanee River, far, far away) is the state song of what state?

Florida

b. Home on the Range (Oh, give me a home where the buffalo roam, Where the deer and the antelope play) is the state song of which state?

Kansas

Trivia for Travelers Round 17

1. In August 1983, CBS records reported that this music artist had sold more than 100 million albums worldwide, recording in six different languages. Who was he?

Julio Iglesias

2. Name the capital city of each of these nations:
a. Bosnia
b. Chile
c. Saudi Arabia

Sarajevo
Santiago
Riyadh

3. Identify four U.S. capital cities named for French words or people?

Montpelier, Vermont / Pierre, South Dakota / Baton Rouge, Louisiana / Des Moines, Iowa

4. Identify these English islands:
a. Named for humanity
b. With a silly name
c. Sounding like a color

Isle of Man
Scilly Isles
Isle of Wight

5. Which non English-speaking nation lies closest to Australia?

Papua, New Guinea

6. Which province of Canada has the highest population?

Ontario, 12 million

7. What region of the world has the largest male / female ratio - where men most outnumber women?

Countries in the Middle East, as United Arab Emirates, Qatar, Bahrain, Brunei, Saudi Arabia

8. What twostrategic bodies of water that begin with the letter B lie closest to Istanbul, Turkey?

Bosporus and the Black Sea

9. The United States is divided into states. How are each of these countries divided?
a. Canada
b. England
c. France

Isle of Man
Sicily Isles
Isle of Wright

10. What three countries occupy the world's third-largest island, Borneo?

Indonesia / Malaysia / Brunei

Trivia for Travelers Round 18

1. Four-letter city names in Europe:
a. City in Republic of Ireland
b. Roman thermal site in England
c. French city closer to Geneva than Paris

Cork
Bath
Lyon

2. Tourists from all over the world visit Jordan to see what 2000 year old city of temples and tombs carved into red-rock by the Nabateans, masters of desert trade?

Petra

3. North American waters:
a. Near what South Dakota city can you visit beautiful waterfalls of the Sioux River?
b. Which impressive river forms the border between Oregon and Washington before pouring into the Pacific Ocean?

Sioux Falls
Columbia River, flowing about 1,947 km. (1,210 mi.)

4. What Pacific islands west of Ecuador are famous for giant tortoises, and which scientist in 1835 collected important scientific data there?

Galapagos Islands / Charles Darwin

5. It is possible to drive entirely across the United States, from San Francisco to New York, on one Interstate highway, the route numbered what?

Route 80

6. He was one of the world's most prolific painters. In his 78-year career he produced over 150,000 paintings, designs, prints, book illustrations, sculptures, and ceramics. Who was this artist who died in 1973?

Pablo Picasso

7. The single land mass that contains the continents of Asia and Europe is known by what name?

Eurasia

8. Japan is composed of four large mountainous islands and about 3,000 smaller ones. Name the largest island of Japan.

Honshu

9. Which U.S. state capital city is named after each of the following:
a. A tribe of Indians
b. A body of water
c. A German political leader
d. A character from the Bible

Cheyenne, WY
Salt Lake City, UT
Bismarck, N.D.
St. Paul, Minnesota

10a. In terms of area, what is Australia's largest state?
b. In terms of population, what is Australia's largest state?

Western Australia / New South Wales

Trivia for Travelers Round 19

1. Identify the national airlines of each of these countries:
a. Netherlands
b. Ireland
c. Israel

KLM
Aer Lingus
El Al

2. On December 8, 1980, John Lennon was murdered outside his apartment building in New York City by a deranged fan. Which person, what apartment building?

Mark David Chapman / Dakota

3. What predominantly Muslim language is the official language of Tanzania and widely used in many countries of eastern Africa?

Swahili

4. The world's tallest cathedral, built from 1248-1560, is Gothic in style, stands over 500 feet tall (160 meters), and is located in what northern European city?

Cologne

5. What type of dog was named after a Mexican state?

Chihuahua

6. What U.S. state is named after the largest of the Channel Islands, lying in the English Channel (La Manche) northwest of France?

New Jersey, named for the island of Jersey, annexed by the Normans in 933, and granted autonomy in 1204.

7. When U.S. college students leave North America to study abroad, what three countries do they most commonly choose?

Any three of: U.K. / Spain / Italy / France

8. Economically, what do all these countries have in common: Canada, Jamaica, New Zealand, Singapore, and Zimbabwe?

All use the dollar as currency

9. What museum of impressionistic art is located in a former train station in Paris?

Musee d'Orsay

10. Journalist Henry Stanley met missionary David Livingstone near the banks of Africa's second longest river. Which one?

Congo

Trivia for Travelers Round 20

1. Which rock music group's 1997 world concert tour was named Bridges of Babylon?

Rolling Stones

2. One of the oldest and most isolated countries in the world, it reached the zenith of its power in the 13th century, when it controlled much of Europe and Asia. What country is this, population today about 2.5 million?

Mongolia

3. What South American capital city lies almost exactly on the equator?

Quito, Ecuador

4. What Asian city has claimed all of the following: World's Busiest Seaport, World's Finest Airport and World's Tallest Hotel?

Singapore

5. Residents of what country call their capital Teguc, short for Tegucigalpa?

Honduras

6. After Mexico City, which two cities of the world have the largest population of Mexicans?

Guadalajara / Los Angeles

7. Which continent is about half as large as Asia?

North America ... Asia is 44 million square kilometers / North America is 24 m. sq. km.

8. What country was named after the Latin word for south?

Australia - auster, austr meaning south

9. What Asian capital city name contains three consecutive dotted letters?

Beijing

10. What is the easternmost European city that is capital of a country?

Moscow

School Events

School Events
School Events Round 1

1. Which insect creates food commonly eaten by humans?

Honeybees

2. Who is the male hero of the fairy tale Cinderella?

Prince Charming

3. June 6, 1944 is known as D-Day, when 5,000 Allied ships invaded the coastline in what part of France?

Normandy - the final drive to liberate Europe was under way

4. The name of what body of water means peaceful or tranquil?

Pacific Ocean

5. What is inside each kernel of popcorn that makes it pop when heated?

Moisture or Water

6. What swimming stroke is named after an insect?

Butterfly

7. It's an eight letter word: Good students have it and nice banks give it. What is it?

Interest

8. These people all ran against each other for President in 1912: Theodore Roosevelt, William Howard Taft, and Woodrow Wilson. Who won?

Woodrow Wilson / 28th President (1913-1921)

9. Give the first names of the five original Spice Girls.

Emma (Bunton), Victoria (Beckham), Melanie (Chisholm) and Melanie (Gulzar) Geri (Halliwell)

10. What are two common references to students named after parts of our head?

Brain / Pupil

School Events Round 2

1. In what children's game do players toss a small object into numbered squares, then skip through the spaces to retrieve the object?

Hopscotch

2. What artist painted the Mona Lisa?

Leonardo da Vinci

3. An interrogative sentence ends with what kind of symbol?

Question mark

4. What fruity phrase refers to your source of pride, the object of your love and affection?

Apple of your eye

5. Most people have 20 of these, but in 1921 a boy born in England had 29 of them. What were they?

Fingers and toes

6. Is light-year a measure of speed, time, or distance?

Distance - that light travels in a year

7. Which tragic mythological king unknowingly killed his father and married his mother?

Oedipus

8. How many active players does each team field in a soccer match?

11

9. To search for land, Noah sent what two kinds of birds out from the ark?

Raven / Dove

10. A 19th century mathematician once stated that he was x years old in the year x^2. In what year was he born?

1806
x = 43 years old
x^2 = 1849 year born

School Events Round 3

1. A joey is the baby of what animal?

Kangaroo

2. In what two sports can a perfect game occur?

Baseball (no batter reaches first base) / Bowling (12 strikes in a row for a score of 300)

3. In the film, The Lion King, the voice of the hyena was played by which humorous woman?

Whoopie Goldberg

4. The three largest cities of a certain U.S. state all begin with the letter C. Name the state and three cities.

Ohio / Columbus, Cleveland, Cincinnati

5. What theme park in Billund, Denmark features small-scale copies of towns, landmarks, and animals made from small snapped-together plastic bricks?

Legoland

6. The Magna Carta was signed by King John at Runnymede in June of what year?

1215

7. Give the first names of these Presidents' wives:
a. George W. Bush's wife
b. Jimmy Carter's wife
c. Abe Lincoln's wife
d. James Buchanan's wife

Laura
Rosalyn
Mary Todd
Unmarried (the only one)

8. What high church official has the same name as a bird?

Cardinal

9. What fragrant cosmetic is named for a city in Germany?

Cologne or Köln

10. The classes in a school run from 8:15 a.m. until 3:06 p.m. There are 8 class periods with 5 minutes passing time between classes. How long is each class period?

47 minutes

School Events Round 4

1. What science studies the structure and history of Earth? — Geology

2. What vegetable in the mustard family is named for a European capital city? — Brussels sprouts

3. In alphabetical order, what are the first three countries of the world? — Afghanistan / Albania / Algeria

4. The Harry Potter series enchants kids as well as adults. Who is the author? — J.K. Rowling

5. What is the meaning of the aviation term, Mach 1? — Moving at the speed of sound

6. If you rearrange some of the letters in the word CALIFORNIA, you can spell each of the following:
a. A continent of the world — Africa
b. A country of Asia — Iran
c. A capital city in Africa — Cairo

7. What is the most common livestock (animals raised for commercial purposes) in the world? — Chickens, ranking next are cows and sheep

8. What product used by hikers, campers, military personnel, and astronauts, has been produced since 1891 by the Victorinox company? — Swiss army knife

9. In what year did George Washington become President of the United States? — 1789

10. If a family has three children, what's the probability that at least two of them are girls? — 50%

School Events Round 5

1. What scripture do Muslims consider the words of God revealed to the Prophet Muhammad?

Koran

2. How many oceans border the United States?

3 - Atlantic, Pacific, Arctic

3. At the turn of the millennium, the cable sports network ESPN ranked the greatest athletes of all time. Who were the top three athletes on their list?

#1 Michael Jordan
#2 Babe Ruth
#3 Muhammad Ali

4. Names of animal groupings:
a. A pride is a collection of what proud animal?
b. A murder of is a collection of what kind of birds?
c. A gaggle is a collection of what water animals?

Lions
Crows
Geese

5. Name the five creatures who traveled together down the yellow brick road in The Wizard of Oz.

Dorothy / Scarecrow / Tin Man / Cowardly Lion / Toto

6. Which two people signed the Declaration of Independence in 1776 and later became U.S. Presidents?

John Adams / Thomas Jefferson

7. The programming language used to prepare documents for the World Wide Web is called HTML, which is the abbreviation for what phrase?

Hyper Text Markup Language - created in 1989 at Cern, in Geneva, Switzerland

8. Which U.S. state's flower is the Mayflower?

Massachusetts

9. The sum of the reciprocals of these two numbers equals ten. One of the numbers is 3 1/2. What is the other?

0 and 1

10. Give the words for hot and cold in each of these languages:
a. Spanish
b. French
c. German

Caliente / Frío
Chaud / Froid
Heiss / Kalt

School Events Round 6

1. Which city in New York is named for an ancient city in Sicily?

Syracuse - founded in the eighth century B.C.

2. In case you are invited to tea with the Queen, what is the proper form of address: is it Your Majesty, Your Highness, or Your Royal Highness?

Your Majesty

3. The fastest animal can move at 220 miles per hour (350 km./hr.). What animal is it?

A bird -the Swift

4. Early Spanish and English explorers brought this edible plant from the Peruvian Andes to Europe in the 16th century. Today it is one of the most popular vegetables in the world. What is it?

Potato

5. In order of area: What are the three largest countries in the world?

Russia / Canada / China

6. In 1893, inspired by the view from atop Pikes Peak, Katherine Lee Bates, Massachusetts educator and author, wrote a song that begins, "O beautiful for spacious skies, for amber waves of grain." What's the title of that song?

America the Beautiful

7. Which three Fox TV series with large ensemble casts were among the most popular television shows of the late 1990s?

Beverly Hills 90201 / Melrose Place / Party of Five

8. Can you name two Summer Olympic sports beginning with the letter F?

Fencing / Field Hockey

9. Famous firsts:
a. The first meal of the day for most people
b. The first sign of the zodiac in astrology
c. The state where the first oil well in the U.S.A. was established

Breakfast
Aries
Pennsylvania

10. The minute hand of a clock is three inches long. How far does the tip of that hand move in one day?

About 453 inches = 37.68 feet - it makes one revolution every hour, so 24 revolutions every day, or $24 \cdot \pi \cdot 6$

School Events Round 7

1. What two colorful rivers meet to form the world's longest river?

Blue / White Nile

2. Which 17th century English physicist and mathematician is said to have discovered the principle of gravity?

Isaac Newton

3. What is the five-letter name for the molten rock that erupts from a volcano, forming lava when it cools?

Magma

4. The Liberty Bell was cast in which city: Philadelphia, Boston, or London?

London

5. Name two women who were wife of one U.S. President and mother of another.

Abigail Adams - wife of John, mother of John Quincy / Barbara Bush - wife of George H., mother of George W.

6. Name all the NBA basketball teams located in California?

Los Angeles Lakers / Los Angeles Clippers / Golden State Warriors / Sacramento Kings

7. Name the author of these classics of children's literature:
a. The Wizard of Oz
b. The Jungle Book
c. The Call of the Wild

L. Frank Baum
Rudyard Kipling
Jack London

8. In the year 1800, the federal government of the United States moved to its newly constructed capital in Washington, D.C., from what city: Boston, New York, or Philadelphia?

Philadelphia

9. An airplane departs at exactly 8:08:08 a.m. and arrives at its destination at exactly 3:03:03 p.m. What is the plane's exact travel time?

6 hours, 5 minutes, 55 seconds

10. Which U.S. President said, "You can fool all of the people some of the time, and some of the people all of the time, but you can't fool all the people all the time"?

Abraham Lincoln

School Events Round 8

1. Which U.S. state calls itself The Breadbasket of America?

Kansas

2. The largest one of these ever discovered came from a giant clam in the Philippines and weighed about 14 pounds. What was it?

A pearl

3. Which two bones in the human body extend from the elbow to the wrist?

Radius / Ulna

4. The phrase, "First in war, first in peace, and first in the hearts of his countrymen," was spoken at the funeral of what person?

George Washington

5. What geometrical computer game was advertised with the slogan: The jigsaw puzzle that fights back?

Tetris

6. Just before the U.S. Civil War, what were the first two states to secede from the Union?

South Carolina / Mississippi

7. In 1945, English author George Orwell published what novel, a fable about the failure of communism?

Animal Farm

8. Name the three bones of the ear.

Hammer / Anvil / Stirrup

9. The name of this occupation contains three consecutive pairs of double letters. What is it?

Bookkeeper

10. If you have 1000 pennies, 1000 nickels, 1000 dimes, 1000 quarters, and 1000 half dollars, then how much do you have altogether?

$910.00: 1000 · .91

School Events Round 9

1. What family was featured in the musical Sound of Music?

Von Trapp or Trapp

2. In which state is John F. Kennedy buried?

Virginia (Arlington Cemetery)

3. The Chinese are generally given credit for how many of these three inventions: the abacus, gunpowder, the magnetic compass?

All three

4. Which of the world's oceans is named after a country?

Indian

5. Which food item is named for a major port of northern Germany?

Hamburger - after Hamburg, Germany

6. This chemical element, symbol S, was known to the ancients; it is the brimstone of the Bible. What do we call it?

Sulfur

7. The Republican Party first appeared on the U.S. Presidential ballot in which of these years: 1826, 1856, or 1860?

1856 - Presidential candidate, John C. Fremont; followed by Lincoln in 1860

8. Which tennis player won the Wimbledon men's' singles championship 7 of the last 8 years of the 20th century?

Pete Sampras

9. Which of these body parts is NOT located in the abdomen: the stomach, intestines, kidney, or liver?

Kidney

10. This question, according to its grouping or parentheses, can have different answers. What is the largest possible solution to the problem: What is half of ten plus two times six?

$42 = (\cdot 5 \cdot 10 + 2) \cdot 6$

School Events Round 10

1. What country lies closest to Greenland?

Canada

2. Which planet was named after the Roman god of war?

Mars - because of its red color

3. What prison in France was stormed by the common people on July 14, 1789?

The Bastille

4. What do we call hollowed-out pumpkins with a face cut into one side?

Jack O'lanterns

5. Can you name three religions beginning with B?

Baptist / Buddhist / Ba'hai

6. What are two common names for jumping, tailless amphibia?

Frogs or Toads

7. The words nadir and zenith: do they have the same or opposite meaning?

Opposite - Zenith is high point, nadir is low point

8. Name the author of these classics of children's literature:
a. Peter Pan
b. A Connecticut Yankee in King Arthur's Court
c. The Secret Garden

J.M. Barrie
Mark Twain
Francis Hodgson Burnett

9. In the 1850s, this escaped slave made 19 secretive trips to the South, and led more than 300 slaves to freedom on the Underground Railroad, despite a bounty of $40,000 on her head. She was never caught. What was her name?

Harriet Tubman

10. What is the largest three-digit number that is divisible by 4, 5, and 6?

960

School Events Round 11

1. Princess Diana, former wife of future King Charles, was Princess of ... what?

Wales

2. Which animals produce pearls?

Oysters

3. A total of fifteen U.S. Presidents were born in the two states that provided the most presidents. What are the states?

Virginia (8) / Ohio (7)

4. Can you name four Spanish speaking countries whose names begin with the letter C?

Chile / Columbia / Costa Rica / Cuba

5. Which large, white puffy clouds are usually a sign of good weather?

Cumulus

6. This person invented dynamite in 1866, and when he died in 1896, left his $9 million fortune to be given away each year as prizes. Who was he?

Alfred Nobel

7. Participants in rhythmic gymnastics primarily use what three objects as props in their performances?

Ball / Hoop / Ribbon

8. In what sport or game are each of these terms used?
a. Frog kick
b. Chip shot
c. Full nelson

Swimming
Golf
Wrestling

9. About 80% of all leather is used to make what product?

Shoes

10. There are 12 teams in a sports league. Every team plays every other team in the league 6 times. How many games are played altogether?

396 - 12 teams play 11 other teams 6 times, divided by 2 to avoid repetition

School Events Round 12

1. Who was the first vice president of the United States?

John Adams

2. What is the world's smallest ocean?

Arctic

3. The U.S. Constitution was completed and ratified in what year?

1787

4. What actually happens when mitosis takes place?

The nucleus of each cell divides into two new nuclei, each of which contains a complete copy of the parental chromosomes

5. See if you can arrange these seven letters into a seven-letter word using all these letters exactly one time: A, E, O, P, R, S, T.

Seaport

6. What father and son acted together in the 1987 film Wall Street as well as the television show The West Wing?

Martin and Charlie Sheen

7. The slowest moving fish looks so interesting that it is represented in Greek mythology. What is it?

Sea horse, ridden by Neptune and other sea gods

8. Shaped like a flat disk, it's about 100,000 light years in diameter, and about 10,000 light years thick. What is it?

Milky Way

9. Identify the female author of each of these works of literature:
a. Little Women
b. Pride and Prejudice
c. Anne of Green Gables

Louisa May Alcott
Jane Austen
Lucy Maud Montgomery

10. If you give me $100, then I will have half as much money as you, but if I give you $100, then you'll have five times as much money as I do. How much does each of us have now?

I have $300, you have $900

School Events Round 13

1. According to the proverb, what brings May flowers?

April showers

2. George W. Bush was the second person to follow in his father's footsteps as President of the United States. Who was the first son of a U.S. President to become a President?

John Quincy Adams - son of John Adams

3. What is the name for two colors whose mixture produces white light, for example red and green?

Complementary colors

4. Painter Vincent Van Gogh was born in 1853, in what country?

Holland or Netherlands

5. Does light travel more quickly through water or through air?

Air

6. In the game of chess, what is the largest number of squares that could be controlled at one time by a horse (knight)?

8

7. Name three countries that begin with J.

Japan / Jordan / Jamaica

8. In March, 1998, NASA announced that an unmanned lunar spacecraft had discovered up to 6 billion tons of ... what ... on the moon?

Ice

9. Name three sports in which the participants move backwards most of the time in attempting to win.

Tug of war / Backstroke / Rowing or Crew

10. If a sports team has won 30 games and lost 20 so far this season, what percentage of their remaining 20 games must they win in order to have a 50% winning season?

25% - to win 35 of 70 total games, they must win 5 of the next 20

School Events Round 14

1. What do we call the black circular opening in the center of the iris of the eye, through which light passes to the retina?

Pupil

2. There are five pairs U.S. Presidents who share the same last name. What are these last names?

Adams (John and John Q.); Harrison (William and Benjamin); Johnson (Andrew and Lyndon); Roosevelt (Theodore and Franklin); Bush (George H. and George W.)

3. What tree and grasshopper have the same name?

Locust

4. In terms of his sports success, his potential as an athlete, and his commercial endorsements, which person did Time Magazine (12/99) call the most ubiquitous (he's everywhere) athlete since Michael Jordan?

Tiger Woods

5. Excluding Antarctica, which continent has the largest percentage of desert land?

Australia

6. The first successful monorail in the U.S. has been running continuously since 1961, in what place?

Disneyland

7. Which inventor in 1793 developed a cotton gin that could do the work of 50 people?

Eli Whitney

8. Which British woman wrote and illustrated The Tale of Peter Rabbit in 1900?

Beatrix Potter (1866-1943)

9. What is the total surface area, in square feet, of a board that is 12 feet long, six inches wide, and two inches thick?

16 1/6 sq. ft.

10. The name of which plant, cultivated for its edible leaves, comes from Latin word for milk, because of its milky juice?

Lettuce - from Latin lac, lact-, milk

School Events Round 15

1. What is measured by the Richter scale?

Intensity of earthquakes

2. The Treaty of Versailles was signed at the end of what war?

World War I

3. What are the two most common ways to say "Good bye" in Italian?

Arrivederci or Ciao

4. What does a transitive verb require to complete its meaning?

A direct object, as: she ate the apple

5. During which U.S. President's term of office did the first man walk on the moon?

Nixon (1969)

6. Russian composer Peter Ilyich Tchaikovsky wrote three ballets. What were they?

The Nutcracker, Swan Lake, and Sleeping Beauty

7. Which person selected the location which later became the District of Columbia (by act of Congress in 1790)?

George Washington

8. In which sport or game does each of these terms apply?
a. Castling
b. Floor exercise
c. Dressage

Chess
Gymnastics
Equestrianism / horse showing - guiding a horse through a series of complex maneuvers

9. In 1997 Sotheby's in New York sold what body part of a fossilized tyrannosaurus rex for $1 million?

Skull or head

10. If one rubber band weighs 40 milligrams, how many of them will weigh one kilogram?

25,000

School Events Round 16

1. What 5-letter word can refer to a spicy Latin dance or a spicy Latin sauce?

Salsa

2. Identify three countries whose names begin with the letter H?

Haiti / Honduras / Hungary

3. In physics, what unit of measure is defined as the ratio of the mass of a substance to its volume, expressed in grams per cubic centimeter or pounds per cubic foot?

Density

4. Who invented the magnetic compass: the Chinese, the Italians or the Germans?

Chinese

5. When water passes through the gills of fish, the fish get what?

Oxygen

6. These rivers eventually flow into what greater bodies of water?
a. Amazon River
b. Potomac River that runs through Washington, D.C.
c. Rhone River

Atlantic Ocean
Chesapeake Bay
Mediterranean Sea

7. In what part of speech does a verb end in "ing" to operate as a noun, such as eating breakfast or answering the phone or walking on the moon?

Gerund

8. Emoticons, or smileys, are a series of typed characters frequently used in e-mails that resemble a face and express the writer's emotion. What does the following represent :-) (colon-dash-right parenthesis)?

Smile

9. According to Norwegian mythology, these repulsive dwarfs who live in hidden places steal children and property and hate noise. What are they called?

Trolls

10. If you add the numerical value of all seven Roman numerals, what is the sum?

1666 = MDCLXVI / M=1000 + D=500 + C=100 + L=50 + X=10 + V=5 + I=1

School Events Round 17

1. How many years is the term of office of a U.S. senator?

6 years

2. What planet in our solar system has the shortest day - only 9 hours and 55 minutes?

Jupiter

3. What part of the Bible is known as the Decalogue?

10 Commandments

4. Which city is home to each of these universities:
a. Brown University?
b. University of Michigan?
c. Vanderbilt University?

Providence, RI
Ann Arbor, MI
Nashville, TN

5. Which two people signed the U.S. Constitution on September 17, 1787, and later became U.S. Presidents?

George Washington /
James Madison

6. Which hero of Daniel Defoe's 1719 novel was stranded and survived on a small tropical island for 24 years?

Robinson Crusoe

7. Which three major league baseball players hit the most home runs during the decade of the 1990s?

Mark McGuire /
Ken Griffey Jr. /
Barry Bonds

8. What do the A&M abbreviate in the name Texas A&M University?

Agricultural and
Mechanical

9. What is the minimum number of tennis shots that could be hit by both players in a complete set of tennis?

36, the winner needs 12 shots to win three games and loser needs 24 shots to lose three games

10. A snail climbs five inches up a vertical wall each day, but slips four inches down the wall each night. If it starts climbing on the beginning of the first day, on which day will it reach the top of a wall that is 30 inches high?

26th day

School Events Round 18

1. What is the world's only city located in two continents?

Istanbul, Turkey

2. Common table sugar comes primarily from what two plants?

Sugar cane / Sugar beets

3. What kind of thin, wispy, feathery looking clouds, located four to twelve miles up, are usually the first sign that a weather front is approaching?

Cirrus

4. In 1808, the U.S. government prohibited the importation into the U.S. of what?

Slaves

5. From the French term chatepelose, meaning "hairy cat," comes the appropriate name of what insect?

Caterpillar

6. Which four U.S. states meet at one point, called the Four Corners?

Arizona / Colorado / New Mexico / Utah

7. Name the authors of each of these fictional works related to the sea:
a. Moby Dick
b. The Old Man and the Sea
c. Jaws

Herman Melville
Ernest Hemingway
Peter Benchley

8. By what name do we call the series of European power struggles fought from 1618-48?

The Thirty Years' War

9. In a single-elimination sports tournament beginning with 64 teams, how many games are played altogether until only one team, the champion, remains?

63 - one game for each losing team

10. Called the world's most successful board game, it was unveiled in 1935, has sold more than 200 million copies in 26 languages. What is it?

Monopoly

School Events Round 19

1. Was Abraham Lincoln assassinated during his first or second term of office?

Second

2. What do we call those cells in the retina that respond to low levels of light and allow seeing in the dark?

Rods

3. Ralph Nader has been a lawyer, consumer advocate, and presidential candidate with which party?

Green

4. Name the authors of each of these written works:
a. Catch-22
b. Don Quixote
c. Little Women

Joseph Heller
Cervantes
Louisa May Alcott

5. Which British author created a world of elves, orcs, ents, and of course hobbits, and what is the title of his famous trilogy?

J.R.R. Tolkien / Lord of the Rings

6. Identify the sound each of these animals make:
a. Goose
b. Donkey
c. Elephant

Honk
Bray
Trumpet

7. This sport, invented in the U.S.A. in 1895, is played in every country of the world, indoors or out, by men or women, with various number of players on a side. It became an official Olympic sport in 1964. What is it?

Volleyball - it can be played with two, three, four, or six players on a team

8. The world's highest waterfall, 980 m. (3,212 ft) high, has what heavenly name, and is located in which country?

Angel Falls / Venezuela

9. The mathematical term googol is equivalent to 10 raised to what power?

100

10. What was the name of King Arthur's sword?

Excalibur

School Events Round 20

1. What is the title of the highest priest of Tibetan Buddhism?

Dalai Lama

2. Three kids put up their own money to make a lemonade stand: the first kid puts up $6, second $3, and the last $1. If they take in $100 and share the profits equally, how much of the $100 will go to the first kid?

$36.00 - each kid makes $30 profit and gets back original investment: 1st kid takes $36, second kid $33, third kid $31

3. Abraham Lincoln had two vice presidents: the first had H.H. as initials, and the second became President upon Lincoln's death. Who were they?

Hannibal Hamlin / Andrew Johnson

4. Which two South American countries border neither the Atlantic nor the Pacific Ocean?

Paraguay / Bolivia

5. Which kindly and generous 4th century Greek bishop is associated with the Christmas season?

Saint Nicholas

6. Which musical instrument, found in most symphony orchestras, is named after a country?

French Horn

7. The largest type of living bird can be 9 feet in height and weigh 350 lbs. (160 kgs.). What kind of bird is it?

Ostrich

8. Shortly after he earned the NBA 1997 Rookie of the Year award, he was arrested in Virginia for drug and firearms possession. Since then he has released controversial rap music albums and became Most Valuable Player for the 2000-2001 season. Who is he?

Allen Iverson

9. After the American Civil War, 15,000 freed slaves emigrated to what African country?

Liberia

10. His Presidential inauguration speech in winter, 1841 took well over an hour to read, during which time he caught a chill that led to pneumonia and death a month later. Name this ninth U.S. President who had the shortest term of office.

William Henry Harrison

School Events Round 21

1. What is the main food product for about half the people of the world?

Rice

2. Of the original thirteen U.S. states, which one was farthest south?

Georgia

3. How many planets in our solar system are smaller than the Earth?

4

4. On a large hill in the city of Athens, you can find a 2400 year old temple. What is it called, and on which hill is it located?

Parthenon / Acropolis

5. This fictional character had an accident. He lost his seating on a lofty perch, and despite efforts by government representatives, he could not be relieved of his injuries. Who was he?

Humpty Dumpty

6. The name of which U.S. President rhymes with one of Santa's reindeer?

Nixon / Vixen

7. Which of these countries has the largest area, and which has the smallest - China, Brazil, or United States?

Largest, China / Smallest, Brazil

8. In alphabetical order, who is the first listed member of the Hall of Fame in each of these sports?
a. Basketball
b. Baseball

Kareem Abdul-Jabbar
Hank Aaron

9. This vitamin, which helps maintain the skin, eyes, healthy bones and teeth, is delivered by milk, eggs, butter, vegetables, and liver. Which vitamin is it?

A - also called Retinol

10. What is the tallest mountain in the United States?

Mount McKinley, also called Denali

School Events Round 22

1. The word opus, meaning work in Italian, has two plurals: one is opuses, but more interestingly, the other is what?

Opera

2. A few questions about the Wizard of Oz:
a. Name five creatures who danced and sang their way down the yellow brick road.

Dorothy / Scarecrow / Tin Man / Cowardly Lion / Toto The Dog

b. At film end Dorothy clicks her heels and utters what chant?

"There's no place like home"

c. Which actress played the role of the Wicked Witch of the West?

Margaret Hamilton

3. How many whole numbers between 1 and 199 begin or end with the digit 2?

29 of them: 2,12,21-29,32,42,52,62,72,82,92,102,112,122,132,142,152,162,172,182,192

4. The first formal schools were created in the fifth century B.C. in what country?

Greece

5. If all the state capital cities in the U.S.A. were listed in alphabetical order, what would be first two?

Albany, NY / Annapolis, MD

6. Where is the human body do you find the hammer, anvil, and stirrup?

Ear

7. What are the opening words of the U.S. Constitution?

"We the people of the United States"

8. How many teeth do turtles have?

None

9. President John F. Kennedy was born in what city, and died in what city?

Brookline, MA or Boston / Dallas

10. What comedian created the voice of Bugs Bunny?

Mel Blanc

School Events Round 23

1. What mysterious, hairy, human-like animal lives in the high Himalayan mountains?

Abominable Snowman / also called Yeti

2. What is the hardest substance known to humans?

Diamonds

3. Who was the first President to visit all the existing states of the United States while in office?

George Washington - visited all 13 existing states between 1789 and 1791

4. How many bones are there in the human body?
b. Of these bones, about one-fourth of them are located in what part of the body?

206
In the feet

5. To identify this U.S. state and its capital city, you must use 4 four letter words. What is it?

Salt Lake City, Utah

6. In 1876, Maria Spelternia was the first woman to cross what on a high wire?

Niagara Falls

7. Which letter begins more words in the English language than any other letter?

S

8. This is the world's oldest organized college sport. In England every year since 1841, Oxford and Cambridge Universities have competed in which sport?

Rowing

9. Can you name three U.S. states whose spellings contain either the letters X or Z?

Texas / New Mexico / Arizona

10. What three animals appear in the nursery rhyme Hey Diddle Diddle?

Cat / Cow / Dog - Hey diddle diddle, the cat and the fiddle
The cow jumped over the moon

School Events Round 24

1. Did Benjamin Franklin sign the Declaration of Independence, the U.S. Constitution, both or neither?

Both

2. In November, 1992, Carole Moseley Braun, from Illinois, became America's first what?

First African-American female U.S. senator

3. The most common gas in the Earth's atmosphere is which of the following: nitrogen, oxygen, ozone, or carbon dioxide?

Nitrogen 78% Oxygen 21%, carbon dioxide <1%.

4. Would the word its need an apostrophe in the following sentence? A dog looked for its owner?

No - it's is only used for the contraction it is

5. Which animal supposedly started the great Chicago fire of 1871?

Mrs. O'Leary's cow

6. Which classic novel opens with these lines, and who was the author? "It was the best of times, it was the worst of times. It was the age of wisdom, it was the age of foolishness."

A Tale of Two Cities / Charles Dickens

7. One of the most evil rulers of all time, who lived in Romania around 1460, was known for killing thousands of his enemies in a cold blooded manner. His name was Vlad, sometimes known as Vlad the Impaler, but the people called him by the Romanian name for the Devil. What was it?

Dracula

8. Name any four of literature's Three Musketeers.
b. Which writer, in 1844, created them?

Athos / Porthos / Aramis / D'artagnin
Andre Dumas

9. Regarding the caloric content of common fruits:
a. The fruit with the most calories, over 700 calories per pound, is the oily fruit of trees found in South America. Which one is it?

Avocado

b. The fruit with the least calories, around 70 calories per pound, grows on a vine, and is commonly is eaten as a vegetable. What is it?

Cucumber

10. If the U.S. President and vice president should die, resign, or otherwise become unable to continue in office, what political position would assume the office of President of the United States?

Speaker of the House of Representatives

School Events Round 25

1. Regarding metric system prefixes:
a. What prefix signifies one-thousand metric units?
b. What prefix represents one million metric units?
c. What prefix stands for one-tenth of a metric unit?

Kilo...
Mega
Deci..

2. He was a lecturer in mathematics at Oxford, and in 1865, produced the children's classic known as Alice's Adventures in Wonderland. What was his pen name and his real name?

Lewis Carroll / Charles Lutwidge Dodgson

3. All of the first six U.S. Presidents were born in either Virginia or Massachusetts. The 7th President was born rather far away from Massachusetts. Who was he, and in what state was he born?

Andrew Jackson / South Carolina

4. Locations of Shakespearean plays:
a. Hamlet is set in what country?
b. Macbeth takes place in what country?
b. Romeo and Juliet are lovers in what city?
d. Othello is a general commanding the forces of what city?

Denmark
Scotland
Verona, Italy
Venice

5. What is the northernmost city with major league baseball team, in the U.S. or Canada?

Seattle

6. Insects like bees, moths, and beetles go through a number of stages of growth. What are the names of the two intermediate stages between the egg stage and the adult stage?

Larva / pupa

7. The word smog is a combination of what two words?

Smoke and fog

8. This indoor sport originated in Ireland in the 16th century, evolving from a method of self defense. If players are not careful, they can get really hurt. What sport?

Darts

9. The headquarters of NATO, North Atlantic Treaty Organizations, is located in which country?

Belgium

10. Whose portrait is shown on a U.S. 10¢ coin (dime)?

Franklin D. Roosevelt

School Round 26

1. What has four eyes and is 2000 miles long?

Mississippi River

2. "Honor thy Father and thy Mother" is what numbered Commandment?

5th Commandment

3. What singing group was voted, in pop music polls, Britain's favorite group in 1997, but Britain's least favorite group in 1999?

Spice Girls

4. What swimming pool game is named after an explorer?

Marco Polo

5. Rub a dub dub, Three men in a tub: who were they?

Butcher / Baker / Candlestick maker

6. The claim that the universe began billions of years ago in a single explosion is called what?

Big Bang Theory

7. Who wrote the Koran?

Muhammad

8. Computers:
a. How many bytes of information make up one K?

b. How many K of memory make up one megabyte?

1024 Kilobytes: kilo means 1,000
1024 Mega = one million. Mega, from megas, meaning great, in Greek

9. The world record for this athletic feat was set by Brazilian Ricardinho Neves in 1994. Using his feet, his body and his head, he did what for 19 hours?

Juggled a soccer ball

10. Identify these mathematics formulas:
a. For the area of a circle
b. For the area of a triangle
c. For the volume of rectangular box

πr^2
$BH \div 2$
$L \cdot W \cdot H$

School Round 27

1. Can you name three sports that begin with B, but don't contain the word ball?

Boxing / Bullfighting / Badminton / Billiards

2. What two symbols are found on pirate flags?

Skull and crossbones

3. What Shakespearean play from 1603 features the question "To be or not to be"?

Hamlet -the Tragedy of Hamlet, Prince of Denmark

4. What's the shortest contraction in English?

I'm or I'd

5. How do you write the number 2000, in Roman numerals?

MM

6. Which part of the human body, if stretched to its full length, would measure about 22 feet in length?

Small intestine

7. This food product, invented in the late 1800s by a St. Louis physician to provide nourishment for his toothless patients, is enjoyed today by kids and grown-ups alike. What is it?

Peanut butter

8. What German engineer invented the diesel engine?

Rudolf Diesel

9. Which actor shouted, "Show Me the Money!" in what movie?

Cuba Gooding, Jr. as Rod Tidwell in the film Jerry Maguire, played by Tom Cruise

10. What is the minimum number of baseball players (from both teams) who could come to bat in a 9-inning baseball game that ends with the score 1-0?

52 - The winning team could have 25 batters in 8 innings (24 outs and one home run), while the losing team would have 27 batters out in 9 innings.

School Round 28

1. How many players are on each side in each of these sports?
a. Soccer / Football
b. Ice hockey
c. Cricket?

11
6
11

2. How many PAIRS of PRIME numbers add up to 100?

There are six pairs:
3+97, 11+89,
17+83, 29+71,
41+59, 47+53

3. What can be found in some, but not all, human bodies, and some, but not all, books?

Appendix

4. Which of the following is true: Worker ants can carry up to 20, 40, or 50 times their own body weight?

Up to 50 times

5. It's possible to drive through two adjacent U.S. states whose capital cities are named after U.S. Presidents. Name the states and capitals.

Nebraska (Lincoln) and Missouri (Jefferson City)

6. Since the early twentieth century, near the end of major league baseball games, fans have observed what tradition, and what song has been sung?

Seventh inning stretch / Take Me Out to the Ballgame

7. Not commonly found on Earth, they could be the most common features of the moon. What are they?

Craters

8. Where does the Roman Catholic pope live?

The Vatican - an independent state within the borders of Rome

9. Which was invented latest: the knife, the fork, or the spoon?

Fork

10. Who is the star of the hit film series, Austin Powers, and what other role does he play in the film?

Mike Myers / Dr. Evil

School Round 29

1. During the Civil War, were each of these states officially part of the Union or Confederate States:
a. Maryland?
b. Missouri?
c. Kentucky?

Union
Union
Union

2. Was it Benjamin Franklin or William Shakespeare who said, "Neither a borrower nor a lender be"?

Shakespeare, in Hamlet

3. There are 20 kids. The first kid can eat 10 jellybeans, and each kid can eat 2 more jellybeans than the previous kid. How many jellybeans can they eat altogether?

580

4. Can you name a professional baseball team, football team, and hockey team, all named after sea creatures?

San Jose Sharks / Miami Dolphins / Florida Marlins / ... More?

5. The Statue of Liberty holds her torch in which hand?

Right

6. What type of animal can grow to 10 meters in length while living inside a human being?

Tapeworm

7. Name the villain in each of these stories:
a. Peter Pan
b. Oliver Twist
c. Shakespeare's Othello

Captain Hook
Fagin
Iago

8. It is said that the Star Wars robot C3PO was designed after what character from the Wizard of Oz?

Tin Man

9. How many voyages did Columbus make to the new world?

Four

10. Give the titles of each of these Tom Cruise films:
a. 1996: He played the role of what sports agent
b. 1993: He plays a new lawyer who takes on a corrupt company
c. 1983: A normal kid throws a wild house-party while his parents are on vacation

Jerry McGuire
The Firm
Risky Business

School Round 30

1. If there are 16 telephone poles in a straight line, each pole 80 meters from the next, how far is it from the first pole to the last?

1200 meters

2. Name an NBA (basketball) team named after a bird.

Atlanta Hawks ... More?

3. Regarding Great Lakes:
a. Which is the largest?
b. Which is the deepest?
c. Which is highest in elevation?

Lake Superior
Lake Superior
Lake Superior

4. Is Earth closer to the sun in summer or winter in the Earth's northern hemisphere?

Winter

5. Give the expanded form of these Internet abbreviations.
a. WWW
b. HTML

World Wide Web
Hyper Text Markup Language

6. Who was the first U.S. President to be impeached?

Andrew Johnson, impeached by the House of Representatives in 1868, eventually acquitted by one vote in the Senate

7. Some of the characters that Alice met in Wonderland were: (fill in the missing words)
a. ... Rabbit
b. ... Cat
c. ... Turtle

White
Cheshire
Mock

8. Who was the first Roman emperor?

Augustus

9. What instrument measures the intensity of earthquakes?

Seismograph

10. If you roll 3 dice at the same time, in how many different ways can you roll a sum of 5?

6 ways = 1,1,3 / 1,2,2 / 1,3,1 / 2,1,2 / 2,2,1 / 3,1,1

Categories

Animals, Events, Food, Great Films,
World History, Literature, People,
Rock 'n' Roll, Science, Sports

Categories
Animals Round 1

1. Most insects go through two growth stages between egg and adult. What are they?

Larva / pupa

2. Which one of these animals does not represent a Chinese year? Dog, Pig, Elephant, or Horse?

Elephant

3. This venomous lizard with a frightening name inhabits dry regions of the southwest United States and western Mexico, and is named after a river. What is it called?

Gila Monster

4. What breed of black, hornless beef cattle are named after two counties of Scotland?

Aberdeen Angus

5. What is the biological name for those animals capable of living both on land and in water?

Amphibian

6. This breed of small dog originated in Tibet, and is named after the capital city. Which dog?

Lhasa Apso, named after the capital of Tibet, Lhasa.

7. What do we call the edible meat of fully grown sheep?

Mutton

8. This slow-moving, plant-eating animal is considered longest-living animal - it can live up to 150 years! What is it?

Tortoise

9. The largest mammal in South America, related to the horse and the rhinoceros, has a heavy body, short legs, and a long, fleshy, upper lip. What animal is this?

Tapir

10. An anaconda is what kind of animal?

Snake

Animals Round 2

1. Name the baby for each of these animals: For example, cat-kitten
a. Deer
b. Elephant
c. Kangaroo

Fawn
Calf
Joey

2. What are the three most common types of animal livestock on U.S. farms?

Chickens 400 million / Cattle 110 million / Swine (Pigs/Hogs) 60 million

3. This dog is a relentless pursuer, and has a keen sense of smell. However, it is considered the least alert dog, and the least likely to succeed as a watchdog. What kind of dog is it?

Bloodhound

4. In what manner can dolphins kill a shark?

Strike or Butt with their noses

5. Give two other names for the animal sometimes known as the whistle pig.

Groundhog / Woodchuck

6. When animals sleep all winter, they hibernate. What do we call it when they sleep all summer?

Estivate

7. Identify these English phrases related to canines:
a. The person with the highest authority
b. A turned-down corner of a page in a book
c. Ruthlessly competitive

Top dog
Dog-ear
Dog-eat-dog

8. What word, meaning a worrisome burden, is named for a type of sea bird?

Albatross

9. Which European songbird is noted for the melodious song of the male at night during the breeding season?

Nightingale

10. Longhaired hunting dogs known as setters are mostly named after two countries. Name these dogs.

English / Irish Setters

Animals Round 3

1. What tropical lizard has the ability to change colors?

Chameleon

2. What large mammal is considered the stupidest?

Camel

3. What country has a Bill of Rights for cows?

India

4. The largest mammal that ever lived weighs more than 100 tons. What kind of animal is this?

Blue whale

5. What animal is named for its metal-like covering of bony plates?

Armadillo

6. What's the difference between a turtle and a tortoise?

Turtles live in water or land / tortoises only on land

7. What do we call the recently hatched, larva form of a butterfly?

Caterpillar

8. What is the largest member of the cat family?

The tiger

9. What animal, adapted to life in the high altitudes, provides milk, meat, wool and leather to herders in Mongolia and Tibet?

Yaks

10. What two breeds of dog are most commonly used as seeing-eye dogs or guide dogs for the blind?

German shepherds / Labrador retrievers, golden retrievers

Animals Round 4

1. The loudest insect makes a sound that can be heard over a quarter of a mile away. What insect is this?

Cicada

2. Identify two extinct elephants whose names begin with M.

Mammoth / Mastodon

3. It has been called the most destructive insect in the world. It can consume 20,000 tons of grain and vegetation in a day. It's even mentioned in the Bible. What insect is it?

Locust

4. In the insect world, certain male bees have the enviable task of performing no work. Their primary function is to mate with the queen bee. What are they called?

Drones

5. About half of the world's 20 million camels are found in two countries whose names begin with S. What countries are they?

Somalia / Sudan

6. The annual festival in Surin, Thailand (250 miles north of Bangkok) features amazing work performed by what trained animals?

Elephants

7. What rather large dog was named for the German breeder who developed it in the latter half of the 19th century?

Doberman pinscher

8. What is the only kind of deer whose females have antlers?

Reindeer

9. With a wingspan of about three meters (ten feet), what is the largest bird in the Western Hemisphere?

Condor

10. What strong and courageous animal, that can be a guard dog, police dog, even a killer dog, was named for a city in Germany?

Rottweiler

Categories
Events Round 1

1. During a 1997 heavyweight boxing championship, Mike Tyson took a bite from the ear of what fighter?

Evander Holyfield

2. In 1947 a Norwegian ethnographer sailed from Peru to Polynesia on a primitive balsa raft to show that South Americans could have settled Pacific islands. Who was he, and what was the name of his raft?

Thor Heyerdahl / Kon-Tiki

3. Tom Hanks won the Best Actor Oscar two years in a row, for his roles in what 1993-1994 films?

Philadelphia 1993 / Forrest Gump 1994

4. It was the largest propeller airplane ever made, and belonged to Howard Hughes. What was its name?

Spruce Goose

5. What are the only two Asian cities to host the Winter Olympics?

Nagano 1998, Sapporo, Japan 1972 (Data 2002)

6. This natural event in May of 1980 in the northwestern part of the United States destroyed 100 square miles of forests, caused a 250 m.p.h. avalanche of snow, and left 66 people dead or missing. What was it?

Volcanic eruption of Mount St. Helens

7. Who was Russia's first woman in space, and who was America's? By how many years did the Russian precede the American into space?

Valentina Tereshkova 1963, Sally Ride 1983 (20 years)

8. On December 10, 1953, the first Playboy magazine was released. Which well-known woman was the first playmate?

Marilyn Monroe

9. At the end of the 20th century, TV Guide Magazine published their list of the 100 Most Memorable Moments in TV History. Which live news event was voted number one on the list?

Neil Armstrong walking on the moon, July 20, 1969

10. When it was unveiled in 1982, one speaker at the ceremony said, "Thank you, America, for finally remembering us." What was it?

Vietnam Memorial, in Washington, D.C.

Events Round 2

1. What February 9, 1964 television broadcast, featuring what musical group, was viewed by 73 million people, gaining the highest ratings in TV history up to that time?

Beatles, first appeared on the Ed Sullivan Show

2. These events occurred in years ending with 9. Name the years:
a. First televised Emmy Awards
b. The St. Valentine's Day Massacre, when seven members of the Bugs Moran gang were rubbed out, probably by the Al Capone gang
c. Paul Gauguin completed his painting, Two Tahitian Women

1949
1929

1899

3. On August 16, 1920, baseball player Raymond Chapman set a baseball statistic that every player and fan hopes will never be equaled. What was it?

Only player killed during a game

4. Name the city that hosted each of these Summer Olympics:
a. 1996: North America
b. 1992: Europe
c. 1988: Asia

Atlanta
Barcelona
Seoul, South Korea

5. Which European adversaries signed a 1998 treaty to end a long-standing bloody conflict?

Irish Catholics and British Protestants in Northern Ireland

6. Her name is Heather Whitestone, from Birmingham, Alabama, and she has a major disability. This did not, however, keep her from winning the Miss America Pageant in September, 1994. What is her disability?

Deaf

7. On April 15, 1974, what wealthy young lady helped rob the Hibernia bank in San Francisco?

Patty Hearst

8. When in June 1963, 26-year-old Valentina Tereshkova did this 48 times, she became the first woman ever to do this, even once. What did she do?

Orbit the earth, aboard Vostok 6

9. Which comedian was the first to depart from the original Saturday Night Live TV troupe?

Chevy Chase

10. In 1969 consumer advocate Ralph Nader warned society of a new cause of impaired hearing in humans. What was he warning us about?

Very loud rock music

Events Round 3

1. What modern engineering wonder was painstakingly constructed from 1904-1914?

Panama Canal

2. According to the Guinness Book of Records, the most expensive painting ever sold fetched $82 million at Christie's in New York in 1990. A Japanese collector purchased Portrait of Dr. Gachet, painted by whom?

Vincent Van Gogh

3. Each of these events occurred in years ending with 7. Name the year.
a. Charles Lindbergh made his first solo flight across the Atlantic
b. Margarine consumption overtook butter in the U.S.A.
c. Newsweek magazine was launched to compete with Time Magazine

1927

1957
1937

4. In 1993 the central European federation of Czechoslovakia split, in a bloodless revolution, to form what two new republics?

Czech Republic and Slovakia

5. What three countries lead the list of medals won at all summer Olympics games since 1896? (consider the country name at the time of winning)

U.S.A. / U.S.S.R. / Great Britain

6. In 1988, this woman became the first female elected leader of an Islamic country. What is her name and her country?

Benazir Bhutto / Pakistan

7. This baseball player, who played from 1905 through 1926, is considered by many the greatest of all time. He batted over .400 three times, and was an outstanding base stealer. Nicknamed the Georgia Peach, who was he?

Ty Cobb

8. On November 13, 1927, after seven years of construction and $50 million in cost, this major engineering work with a foreign sounding name opened in New York City. What was it?

Holland Tunnel

9. What rather small but tremendously useful item, found in every home today, was invented in 1879, in Menlo Park, New Jersey?

Incandescent lamp (Edison)

10. What newsman was the host of television's first daily network news broadcast?

Walter Cronkite

Events Round 4

1. Which two athletic female relatives, one a long jumper, the other a runner, gained gold medals in the Seoul Olympics of 1988?

Jackie Joyner-Kersee / Florence Griffith-Joyner

2. What two singing cowboy kings died within weeks of each other in 1998?

Roy Rogers / Gene Autry

3. What holiday is celebrated the day after Christmas in many parts of the British Commonwealth?

Boxing Day, when gifts are given to service workers

4. In 1926, Gertrude Ederle became the 6th person ever, but the first woman, to accomplish what athletic challenge?

Swim the English Channel

5. In 1975, North Vietnamese forces overran Saigon, capital of South Vietnam, and renamed it what?

Ho Chi Minh City

6. On October 30, 1938, Orson Welles produced a fictional radio play in the form of an actual news event, that scared millions of listeners into believing it an invasion by Martians.
a. What was the name of this play?
b. In this show, Martians landed close to which well-known college town?

War of the Worlds
Princeton, New Jersey

7. In October, 1957 the U.S.S.R. launched the first artificial satellite, and the U.S.A. followed about four months later. What were the names of these two objects?

Russian: Sputnik / American: Explorer

8. The modern rules of boxing were formulated in 1867 by what British aristocrat and boxing promoter?

Marquess of Queensbury, title of Sir John Sholto Douglas (1844-1900)

9. The lava flowing from what Hawaiian volcanic crater caused the sea to boil in 1986?

Kilauea, on the southeast slope of Mauna Loa

10. Citizens of the United States celebrate July 4 annually to honor what historical event, that occurred in what year?

Adoption of the Declaration of Independence on July 4, 1776

Categories

Food Round 1

1. What is the name of the metal pan with a rounded bottom in which many Chinese dishes are fried and steamed?

Wok

2. What is the heavenly name for the almond flavored sponge cake made from flour, sugar, and egg whites?

Angel food cake

3. What sea food, harvested off the coasts of Alaska, Japan, and Siberia, has a truly royal name?

King crab

4. The MacDonald's Restaurants in New Delhi and Bombay serve the McMaharajah, a hamburger made of what meat?

Mutton, the flesh of fully grown sheep

5. Small, thin, delicious loaves of French bread are called what?

Baguettes

6. This tall, frosted drink made of bourbon, brandy or rum, and flavored with mint leaves is popular in New Orleans. What's the name?

Mint julep

7. Which delicious pastry is named after the Little Corporal?

Napoleon

8. Which American breakfast item is named for a British greeting?

Cheerios

9. What type of cheese is named after a village of southwest England?

Cheddar

10. Literally this word means, in Swedish, bread and butter, or open sandwich, and refers to a large meal featuring a wide selection of foods. What is the word?

Smorgasbord

Food Round 2

1. This nutritious substance secreted by worker bees serves as the only food for the larvae that eventually develop into queen bees. What is it?

Royal jelly

2. What product did the Grey Poupon company begin producing in 1777? (2 words)

Dijon mustard

3. What cocktail, made from rum and lime or lemon juice, is named after the Cuban village where it was first served?

Daiquiri

4. Identify these food-related words:
a. Appetizer of meats, cheese, fish, eaten before meals, literally means before food in Italian. What is it?

Antipasto

b. Type of food tray named after a sluggish woman

Lazy Susan

5. This type of wine mainly used in mixed drinks is flavored with aromatic herbs. Its name comes from old French and German and means wormwood. What is it?

Vermouth

6. Many people consider saffron to be the most expensive cooking spice. Saffron comes from what flower?

Crocus

7. What is the three-word Spanish name for the spicy food dish made from meat, beans, and red peppers?

Chile con carne

8. This is a common riddle about what food item? You throw away the outside, and cook the inside. Then you eat the outside, and throw away the inside.

Corn on the cob

9. Name three types of Indian breads.

Any three of ... Paratha / Naan / Puri / Chapatti / Pappadom...

10. Name the two primary ingredients of the cocktail known as a Bloody Mary.

Vodka / Tomato juice

Food Round 3

1. What three alcoholic beverages are most commonly used to make a martini?

Gin or Vodka with vermouth

2. What do we call the Yiddish dish of finely chopped fish, mixed with crumbs, eggs, and seasonings, cooked in a broth in the form of an oval?

Gefilte fish

3. This form of German sweet bread is first baked, then sliced and toasted. Its name, in German, literally means twice baked. What is it?

Zwieback

4. Identify the countries that lead the world in the production of each of the following:
a. Wine
b. Beer
c. Tea

Italy
U.S.A.
India

5. When a cake recipe includes baking powder or baking soda, the cake achieves a spongy texture due to the release of what chemical?

Carbon dioxide

6. Can you identify the creamy sauce of butter, egg yolks, and lemon juice named after a European country?

Hollandaise

7. International foods:
a. What's the name for the Swiss specialty of bread cubes dipped into melted cheese?
b. What do the Japanese call the dish of deep fried vegetables or seafood?

Fondue

Tempura

8. What is the primary grain in bourbon?

Corn

9. What edible marine treat was William Shakespeare referring to when he said, "The world is my..."?

Oyster

10. In 1776, a tavern keeper in New York mixed rum and juice, and used rooster feathers as an ornament. What did he call this concoction?

Cocktail

Food Round 4

1. What type of small seedless raisin is named for the wife or mistress of an Arabian king or prince?

Sultana

2. The name of what pungent, blue-veined cheese comes from the northern Italian town where it was first made?

Gorgonzola

3a. The world's best caviar supposedly comes from the eggs of what kind of fish?

Sturgeon

b. Perhaps the world's best caviar comes from what body of water north of Iran?

Caspian Sea

4. True or false: White wine is made from white grapes; red wine is made from red grapes.

False: white wine can come from grapes of any color. Red wine includes the skin of the red grapes

5. Two of the world's most expensive coffees are grown in North America. Can you name them?

Jamaican Blue Mountain / Kona (from Hawaii)

6. Name that spicy dish!
a. With the same name as a dance
b. With the same name as a country

Salsa
Chile

7. Name the most common alcoholic beverage made from each of these plants... for example, apples (cider)
a. Potatoes
b. Rice
c. Wormwood (used in the 19th century to make a beverage enjoyed by Impressionist painters)

Vodka or Aquavit
Sake
Absinthe

8. What fishy treat is a great snack food, often eaten raw in Holland and other northern European countries?

Herrings

9. This type of pasta is made in long strands thinner than spaghetti, and its Italian name means little worms. What is it?

Vermicelli

10. There are more than 2,000 varieties of what food item made from ripened curds?

Cheese

Categories
Great Films Round 1

1. Four times in the film, Casablanca, Humphrey Bogart delivers what line?

"Here's looking at you, kid."

2. Some people consider Alfred Hitchcock's 1960 masterpiece, Psycho, the greatest suspense flick of all time. What character kills a woman in the famous shower scene, and which actor and actress played these roles?

Character Norman Bates, played by Anthony Perkins, and Janet Leigh

3. Which 1963 film was banned in Egypt for 20 years because the female star, Elizabeth Taylor, had converted to Judaism?

Cleopatra

4. The Oscar-winning films from 1982 and 1984 were biographies of a politician and a musician. Name these movies.

Gandhi '82 / Amadeus '84

5. The largest-selling album from a movie songtrack ever, and one of the largest selling albums of all time, came from what 1992 Whitney Houston film?

The Bodyguard

6. The 1975 film, One Flew Over the Cuckoo's Nest won the four major Academy Awards for actor, actress, director and film. Name the winning actor, actress, and director.

Jack Nicholson / Louise Fletcher / Milos Forman

7. Early in 2000, the Broadcast Film Critics Association published their list of the top films of the 1990s, and the top two films were directed Steven Spielberg. What were they?

Schindler's List / Saving Private Ryan

8. The first movie ever to win the Academy Award as Best Picture was what 1927 film with a one-word title, set in the skies over France and Germany during World War I?

Wings

9. Name the actresses who starred in each of these films:
a. 1969 - The Prime of Miss Jean Brodie
b. 1979 - An Unmarried Woman
c. 1989 - When Harry Met Sally

Maggie Smith
Jill Clayburgh
Meg Ryan

10. This 1968 film had a $1 million make-up budget, and won a special Oscar for make-up. Most of the characters in the film needed extensive make-up. This film is now considered a science-fiction classic, and led to four sequels

Planet of the Apes

Great Films Round 2

1. What is the title of Spike Lee's 1992 film biography of a black militant? | Malcolm X

2. In this 1986 comedy/horror/musical/dance film, a nebbish working in a flower shop nurtures an unusual new plant, which turns into a Frankenstein. What was the title of this film? Which actor played the role of the nerdy flower shop clerk, and what was the flower's name? | Little Shop of Horrors / Rick Moranis / Audrey the Flower

3. 1966 was a good year for these two sisters. One starred in the film Blow Up, the other got an Oscar nomination for her role in Georgie Girl. Who are they? | Vanessa and Lynn Redgrave

4. The biggest box-office money-makers of 1942 were what acting pair? | Abbott and Costello

5. The largest money-losing film of all time cost over $55 million and grossed less than $2 million. Critics and audiences panned this 3 1/2 hour film. What was the title, and who was the director of this 1980 film about land wars in Wyoming? | Heaven's Gate / Michael Cimino

6. At the end of The Wizard of Oz, Dorothy clicks her heels together and chants what phrase? | "There's no place like home"

7. Name the year each of the famous films was released:
a. High Noon, Moulin Rouge, and Singing in the Rain | 1952
b. Carnal Knowledge, A Clockwork Orange, and Fiddler on the Roof | 1971
c. Forrest Gump, Four Weddings and a Funeral, and Pulp Fiction | 1994

8. Identify the 1961 film that was coincidentally the last film made by both Clark Gable and Marilyn Monroe? | The Misfits

9. Name the actors who have played Presidents in each of these films:
a. 1995: The American President | Michael Douglas
b. 1964: Dr. Strangelove | Peter Sellers
c. 1939: Young Mr. Lincoln | Henry Fonda

10. The Academy-award winning films from 1990 and 1991 contained animal names in the titles. Which films? | Dances with Wolves / Silence of the Lambs

Great Films Round 3

1. For creating the best-kept movie secret of 1992, writer-director Neil Jordan won the Oscar for Best Screenplay, and was nominated for Best Achievement in Directing, and his film was also nominated for Best Picture of the Year. Which film was this?

The Crying Game

2. Charles Laughton and Clark Gable starred in this 1935 Oscar winning film about rebellion on the high seas. Trevor Howard and Marlon Brando starred in the 1962 sequel. What is the title?

Mutiny on the Bounty

3. Name two great films, one from 1975,one from 1983, that included Danny Devito and Jack Nicholson?

One Flew over the Cuckoo's Nest / Terms of Endearment

4. One of the most successful feats of directing occurred in 1939 when one person directed both The Wizard of Oz and Gone With the Wind. Who was he?

Victor Fleming

5. Name the actor or actress who played the title role in each of these films:
a. 1966: Alfie
b. 1943: Madame Curie

Michael Caine
Greer Garson

6. In what 1955 comedy film does Marilyn Monroe stand over a subway grating as the wind blows her skirt up to her face?

Seven-Year Itch, co-starring Tom Ewell

7. Name the character played by Dustin Hoffman in each of these films:
a. The Graduate
b. Midnight Cowboy

Benjamin Braddock/ Ratso Rizzo

8. Name the actor, born in South Africa to British parents, who most often portrayed Sherlock Holmes in films, 14 times in the 1940s?

Basil Rathbone

9a. What actor is founder and president of the Sundance Film Institute?
b. In what western city is the Sundance Film Festival annually held?

Robert Redford

Park City, Utah

10. A certain Charles Dickens novel was turned into film twice: first, a dramatic masterpiece in 1948 which starred

Oliver Twist / Oliver

Great Films Round 4

1. In 1982, the same year that Dustin Hoffman played the role of a woman in the motion picture Tootsie, Julie Andrews played a male singer in which film?

Victor/Victoria

2. Which 1995 film, based on an 1811 Jane Austin novel, starred Emma Thompson and Hugh Grant?

Sense and Sensibility

3. Distinguished British actor Anthony Hopkins played the film role of what U.S. President?

Richard Nixon

4. What two actresses played the same character in the same 1998 film, and won the Academy Awards as Best Actress and Best Supporting Actress for their efforts?

Kate Winslet / Gloria Stuart played the same character, a young and old Rose in Titanic

5. This glamorous, mysterious German movie star, first popular in the 1920s, refused an offer to return to Nazi Germany, and instead became an anti-Nazi propagandist during World War II. Who is she?

Marlene Dietrich

6. One of the three main acting stars of the 1969 film Easy Rider also directed the film. Who was he?

Dennis Hopper

7. What 1988 film starred Tom Cruise and Dustin Hoffman, and who was the director?

Rain Man / Barry Levinson

8. Which three actresses played wives deceived by their philandering husbands in the 1995 film The First Wives' Club?

Bette Midler / Goldie Hawn / Diane Keaton

9. In 1983 The Oscar for Best Supporting Actress went to a woman who played a male photographer. What was the name of the international thriller film and who was the actress?

The Year of Living Dangerously / Linda Hunt

10. Which actors played the following roles in the film, The Wizard of Oz?
a. Cowardly Lion
b. Scarecrow
c. Tin Man

Bert Lahr
Ray Bolger
Jack Haley

Categories
World History Round 1

1. Around 4000 B.C. in the lower Tigris and Euphrates valley, the Sumerians developed what form of wedge-like writing?

Cuneiform

2. When the Great Pyramid was being built, what was the capital of Egypt?

Memphis

3. Which leader of the Greeks in the Trojan War was killed by his wife upon his return from Troy?

Agamemnon

4. What great re-occurring event first took place in the year 776 B.C. in Europe?

Olympic Games

5. Around the first century B.C., what name did the Romans give to the region of the Jews in southern Palestine, today southern Israel?

Judea or Judaea

6. In the year 79 A.D. a prosperous Italian city of villas, temples, theaters, and baths disappeared after the eruption of a volcano. Name the city and the volcano.

Pompeii / Vesuvius

7. Today it's a seaside resort town of southeast England, but in 1066 a major battle raged there. What city is it?

Hastings

8. Legend has it that in the 11th century England's Lady Godiva rode naked on a horse through what the streets of what town, and for what reason?

Coventry, England as a tax protest to persuade her husband, Earl of Mercia, to lower the heavy taxes

9. Considered to be the first book printed with movable type was Gutenberg's Bible, printed around 1455. In which language was it written?

Latin

10. What was the name of the Christopher Columbus' flagship - the ship on which Columbus traveled in his 1492 voyage to the New World?

Santa Maria in the Bahamas

World History Round 2

1. In 1492, the Spanish expelled all Jews from Spain, and rescued the country from Moslem control. What was the last city in Spain controlled by the Moslems?

Grenada

2. This warlike and despotic 15th century Aztec ruler, was overthrown by Spanish conquistador Hernando Cortés, who stole fabulous treasures from him and his people. Who was he?

Montezuma, the last Aztec emperor in Mexico 1502-1520

3. On September 25, 1513, Spanish explorer Vasco de Balboa discovered a large body of water that he named the South Sea, but we call what?

Pacific Ocean

4. The first African slaves were brought to the American colonies in 1619 by what nationality of Europeans?

Dutch

5. From which seaport on the southern coast of Britain did the Mayflower set sail for the New World in 1620, and at what New World location did she land?

Southampton / Plymouth

6. Now illegal in all U.S. states, Rhode Island in 1774 became the first U.S. state to ban what practice?

Slavery

7. The first six Presidents of the U.S. were all born in either Virginia or Massachusetts. The seventh President was the first born outside those two states. Who was he, and in what southern state was he born?

Andrew Jackson / South Carolina

8. This English military hero was killed in 1805 at the Battle of Trafalgar off the coast of Spain, and today his statue stands in the center of Trafalgar Square in London. Who is he?

Admiral Lord Nelson

9. This 1850s war was triggered by a dispute between France, Russia, and Turkey over control of the Holy Places in Palestine, and during this war Florence Nightingale performed her heroic nursing deeds. Name the war?

Crimean War

10. What Scottish missionary and explorer discovered the Zambesi River in 1851, Victoria Falls in 1855, and later searched for the source of the Nile River?

David Livingstone

World History Round 3

1. On June 28, 1914, a young man named Gavril Princip darted out of a crowd in a Bosnian city and fired two bullets into a car, killing what two passengers?

Archduke Franz Ferdinand, heir to the Austro-Hungarian empire, and his wife, the Duchess of Hohenburg

2. What early 20th century Turkish leader abolished the use of the Arabic alphabet, some Islamic traditions, and the wearing of the veil by women in Turkey?

Kemal Atatürk; and he abolished polygamy and the Islamic legal system in Turkey

3. One hundred years ago, the tallest structure in the world was the Eiffel tower. What building, when constructed in 1929, became the tallest in the world, exceeding the Eiffel tower in height?

New York's Chrysler Building

4. September 1, 1939, generally is considered the start of World War II, when Germany attacked what country?

Poland

5. Fidel Castro come to power in Cuba in what year?

1959

6. Of all of Richard Nixon's cronies, assistants, and legal associates, who was the first to spend time in jail due to involvement in the 1970s Watergate scandal?

John Dean

7. Richard Nixon, Gerald Ford, and Jimmy Carter traveled overseas in 1981 to attend the funeral of what person?

Anwar Sadat, the assinated leader of Egypt

8. On January 28, 1986, what space shuttle exploded on take off, and what two female astronauts died on board?

Challenger / Christa McAuliffe / Judith Resnick

9. This amendment to the U.S. Constitution was first proposed in 1789, but only ratified by Congress in 1992 because it's related to them. It's the last of the amendments - the 27th. What does it provide for?

Congress can't change (add to) its own salary while in office

10. Millions of people in this Asian land changed their nationality due to a political agreement on July 1, 1997. What happened?

Hong Kong became part of the People's Republic of China

World History Round 4

1. In 1781 the British forces, under the direction of Charles Cornwallis, surrendered control of the American colonies, after their final defeat in what southern city?

Yorktown, Virginia

2. In the year 79 A.D. a beautiful resort town of villas, temples, theaters, and baths was destroyed by a volcanic eruption in southern Italy. Name the city and volcano.

James Buchanan

3. December 14, 1911, Roald Amundsen was the leader of a Norwegian team, the first to reach what geographic landmark?

South Pole

4. In April, 1912, The Titanic embarked on its fateful voyage - from what southern English port?

Southampton, England

5. What U.S. President, in 1823, declared that the United States would not tolerate intervention by European nations in the affairs of nations in the Americas?

James Monroe - the Monroe Doctrine

6. Around 500 A.D., what holy man converted the Irish to Christianity?

St. Patrick

7. When this engineering wonder was completed in 1883, it connected America's first and third largest cities. What was it?

Brooklyn Bridge, which connected cities New York and Brooklyn; Brooklyn became part of greater New York City in 1898

8. What U.S. navy battleship, named after a state, was sunk by the Japanese at Pearl Harbor on December 7, 1941?

U.S.S. Arizona

9. In 1910, Thomas Edison demonstrated a new invention that he called the kinetophone, a forerunner of what modern machine?

Movie Projector

10. When the Eiffel Tower was completed in 1889, it became the tallest structures in the world, exceeding what two others for that distinction?

Washington Monument, 555 feet (168 meters) / Great Pyramid, 482 feet (146 meters)

Categories
Literature Round 1

1. Ernest Hemingway won the Pulitzer Prize for his 1952 fiction about an aged fisherman and his heroic battle with a giant marlin. What was the title of this novel?

The Old Man and the Sea

2. Who was the author of the 17th century novel, Don Quixote?

Miguel de Cervantes

3. Which northern German city became a tourist attraction because of the legend of the Pied Piper?

Hamelin

4. Her best-known work, an account of her childhood growing up as a black girl in the rural South, is called I Know Why the Caged Bird Sings. Who is the author?

Maya Angelou

5. Around the year 500 B.C., writings by Chinese philosopher Kung Fu-tzu greatly influenced Chinese culture, and later the world. This philosopher was better known to the Western world by his Latin name. What is it?

Confucius

6. In the Shakespearean play King Henry IV, Falstaff says, "Discretion is the better part of...." What?

Valor

7. These nine goddesses of classical mythology presided over learning, the arts and poetry. Greek and Roman writers often began their poems asking for their assistance. Who were they?

Muses

8. This is the plot of what novel by what author: Marooned on a tropical island, a group of English schoolboys attempt to set up a civilized society, but fail, and savagery instead erupts.

Lord of the Flies, by William Golding

9. This 19th century English author who wrote Middlemarch, The Mill on the Floss, and Silas Marner was a woman who used a male nom de plume. Name the author and her pen name.

Mary Ann Evans wrote as George Eliot

10. Who wrote the classic novel of the sea, Moby Dick?

Herman Melville

Literature Round 2

1. What poem, by what writer, begins:
"Under the spreading chestnut tree
The village smithy stands..."

The Village Blacksmith / Henry Wadsworth Longfellow

2. This Indian-born British writer has been living in hiding. His 1988 written work, considered blasphemous by some followers of Islam, caused Iranian Ayatollah Khomeini to call for his death. Name him and his controversial work.

Salman Rushdie / Satanic Verses

3. Which American playright, first popular in the 1940s and 1950s, named himself after a state?

Tennessee Williams, born Thomas Lanier Williams - Glass Menagerie, A Streetcar Named Desire, and Cat on a Hot Tin Roof

4. The only novel published during the lifetime of this Czech Jewish novelist was Metamorphosis, published in 1915. Who was he?

Franz Kafka, (1883-1924)

5. Identify the authors of these 18th-19th century works:
a. Dracula
b. Around the World in 80 Days
c. Candide

Bram Stoker
Jules Verne
Voltaire

6. One of the most significant political works of the 20th century, Mein Kampf, was written in 1924 by which person? Where was he when he wrote it?

Adolf Hitler / in Prison

7. Which 19th century British poet, whose works include The Charge of the Light Brigade, wrote, "It is better to have loved and lost, than never to have loved at all"?

Alfred, Lord Tennyson (1809-1892)

8. The phrase, "Water, water, everywhere, nor any drop to drink..." comes from The Rime of the Ancient Mariner, written by whom?

Samuel Taylor Coleridge

9. In this 8th century epic, considered the first long work of literature in English, our hero struggles against monsters and dragons. What's the title?

Beowulf

10. Which medieval English poet's 1380 work, called Parlement of Foules, takes place "on Seynt Valentynes day, when every fool cometh to choose his mate"?

Geoffrey Chaucer

Literature Round 3

1. Who was the author of the autobiography The Diary of a Young Girl?

Anne Frank

2. According to this children's story, a young duck, constantly mocked by the others for being ugly, grows up to be the most beautiful swan. What's the title and who is the author?

The Ugly Duckling / Hans Christian Andersen

3. This 1920s play is considered the first English play written exclusively for children. It's called Peter Pan.
a. Which Scottish author wrote it?
b. It was a story about a boy who lived in what land where children never grow up?

James Barrie
Never-Never Land

4. This Greek poet from 850 B.C. was blind, so he had to memorize his most famous literary works, including the Iliad and the Odyssey. Who was he?

Homer

5. Which Charles Dickens literary work featured the mean-spirited miserly character named Ebenezer Scrooge?

A Christmas Carol

6. Best-selling books: Name the author:
a. 1936-37: Gone with the Wind
b. 1969: Portnoy's Complaint
c. 1993: The Bridges of Madison County
d. early 2000s: Harry Potter

Margaret Mitchell
Philip Roth
Robert James Waller
J.K. Rowling

7. She is considered an authority on etiquette; in 1922 she wrote the book entitled Etiquette: The Blue Book of Social Usage. Who is she?

Emily Post

8. Can you name the two Shakespearean plays whose titles begin with the word King?

King Lear / King John

9. Who wrote the 1933 autobiography of Alice B. Toklas?

Gertrude Stein

10. This beloved 19th century poem begins with the line "T'was the night before Christmas." What is the original title of this poem, and who wrote it?

A Visit from St. Nicholas / Clement Clark Moore

Literature Round 4

1. Of Dr. Jekyll and Mr. Hyde, which one was cruel and sadistic?

Mr. Hyde

2. After bowling and drinking and carrying on in the mountains with a bunch of dwarves Rip Van Winkle fell asleep.
a. How long did he sleep?
b. What author created the character?

20 years
Washington Irving

3. In 1953, Ernest Hemingway won the Pulitzer Prize for literature, for what novel?

The Old Man and the Sea

4. What is the title of the 1953 play about the Salem Witch Trials, and who was the author?

The Crucible / Arthur Miller

5. The first major American dictionary was published in 1828 by what person?

Noah Webster

6. Name the authors of these 19th century gothic novels:
a. Dracula, written by what English man?
b. Frankenstein, written by what English woman?

Bram Stoker
Mary Shelley

7. The three witches in Shakespeare's Macbeth utter what eerie chant?

"Double, double toil and trouble; fire burn and cauldron bubble."

8. Which authors created each of these pursuers of truth and justice?
a. James Bond
b. Perry Mason
c. Philip Marlowe

Ian Fleming
Earle Stanley Gardner
Raymond Chandler

9. What 19th century French author is known for such adventure novels as Around the World in 80 Days, 20,000 Leagues under the Sea, and Journey to the Center of the Earth?

Jules Verne

10. In 1917, after a printer's error caused all his words to be printed in lower case, this Massachusetts poet continued the practice — and became famous because of it. Who was he?

e.e. cummings
(1894-1962)

Categories

People Round 1

1. Who was the first pilot to fly solo nonstop across the Atlantic Ocean?

Charles Lindbergh in May 1927

2. Mother Theresa, one of the world's most generous people, lived from 1910 to 1997.
a. In which city did she do most of her life's work?
b. Which prize did she win in 1979?
c. What was her nationality?

Calcutta
Nobel Peace Prize / Albanian

3. What Swedish astronomer, in 1742, invented the Centigrade temperature scale?

Anders Celsius

4. What four-year-old boy began taking harpsichord lessons in 1760?

Wolfgang Amadeus Mozart

5. In his 1796 farewell address, what person warned the American citizens about foreign involvement in their young country?

George Washington

6. What legendary 14th century Spanish nobleman and libertine, said to have seduced hundreds of women, is the subject of works of music, literature, and art?

Don Juan, eventually damned for his immoral ways

7. As a youth in Mexico City he was a bullfighter, but his first love was music. He later sang with international opera companies, made recordings, and filled concert halls. One of The Three Tenors, who is he?

Placido Domingo

8. Who was the first European explorer to travel from Europe overland to the Pacific Ocean and what was his home town?

Marco Polo, from Venice

9. Pop musician Gloria Estefan was born in 1957 in what capital city?

Havana, Cuba

10. Supply the last name of each of these people:
a. Military officer and politician Napoleon
b. Artist Rembrandt
c. Singer Madonna

Bonaparte
Van Rijn or Van Ryn
Ciccone

People Round 2

1. What 17th century English mathematician, physicist, and philosopher is considered by many to be the greatest scientist who ever lived?

Isaac Newton (1642-1727)

2. He has purchased properties in London and Windsor, England, Nice, France, and Atlanta, Georgia. His passions include vintage cars, designer clothes, jewels and flowers. Who is this entertainer?

Elton John

3. In his 20s he joined a revolutionary group, was arrested and sentenced to four years of hard labor in Siberia. Later he wrote Crime and Punishment and The Brothers Karamazov (1879-80). Who was he?

Fyodor Dostoevsky (1821-1881) Russian novelist

4. In 1963, Arthur had just completed a mathematics degree at Columbia University while Paul had just dropped out of law school. It was aperfect time for them to begin making music together. Who were they?

Paul Simon and Art Garfunkel

5. TV butlers and waiters:
a. What was the name of Jack Benny's personal valet?
b. Who was the sharp witted butler in TV's Soap?
c. Who was the non-English speaking waiter in Fawlty Towers?

Rochester
Benson
Manuel

6. One of the greatest composers of the Classical period was teacher of Mozart and Beethoven, and wrote the national anthem of Austria. Who was he?

Franz Joseph Haydn (1732-1809)

7. What two Italian-born anarchists were convicted of robbery and murders in Massachusetts in the early 1920s, and put to death in 1927 (to the consternation of liberals and left-wingers who thought they were unjustly convicted)?

Nicola Sacco / Bartolomeo Vanzetti

8. Born in 1954 in Hong-Kong, this actor, writer, producer, and director has been called the world's biggest non-Hollywood movie star. Who is he?

Jackie Chan

9. Which former U.S. President was born in Milton, Massachusetts in 1924?

George H. Bush

10. She was King Arthur's queen and Lancelot's love. Who was she?

Guinevere

People Round 3

1. According to Persian, Indian, and Arabic folk tales, who was the sultan's wife who narrates the 1001 Arabian Nights?

Sheherazade

2. Her name was María Estela Martínez, and she became the first female chief of state in the Americas. By what name do we know her?

Eva Peron, President of Argentina when her husband died in 1974

3. When this versatile actor known for drama as well as comedy was honored by Queen Elizabeth, he preferred to be knighted with his stage name, rather than his real name, Maurice Micklewhite. Who is he?

Michael Caine

4. Some questions about Martin Luther King:
a. He was born in 1929 in which major city?
b. In 1955 he led the black boycott of the transport system of what southern city?
c. He organized the massive civil rights march on Washington in what year?

Atlanta, GA
Montgomery, AL

1963

5. As a young child in the 1950s, she was a singing prodigy in her church choir. She signed a recording contract in 1960, hit the charts in 1967 and became in 1987 the first woman inducted into the Rock and Roll Hall of Fame. Who is she?

Aretha Franklin

6. What 20th century Swiss psychologist classified people as extroverts and introverts, and devised the concept of a feminine side of men and a masculine side of women?

Carl Jung

7. What are the names of Queen Elizabeth's four children?

Charles, Anne, Andrew, Edward

8. In 1812, at the age of three, this young French boy was blinded in an accident. Nevertheless he grew up to be a musician, educator, and inventor of a very useful system for handicapped people. Who was he?

Louis Braille - invented a system of reading for blind people

9. On October 21, 1805, the Battle of Trafalgar was fought near the southwest coast of Spain. In a mere five hours, which British Admiral led the English fleet to victory over the combined French and Spanish navys?

Horatio Nelson

10. Can you name two famous billionaires who died in the year 1976?

Howard Hughes / J. Paul Getty

People Round 4

1. Who was the first person to lose a U.S. Presidential election?

Thomas Jefferson, who lost to John Adams in 1796; George Washington ran unopposed

2. Referring to her childhood in the 1950s she said, "The only thing I ever really wanted was to be normal. To be average. To be able to run, jump, and play and do all the things other kids did in my neighborhood." Crippled at age 11, she went on to become an Olympic medal winner in track and field by age 20. Who was she?

Wilma Rudolph (1940-1994)

3. Who was Abraham Lincoln's wife?

Mary Todd Lincoln

4. What person starred in a Christmas special on television each holiday season from 1950 to 1994?

Bob Hope

5. In what year did Prince Charles and Princess Diana marry?

1981

6. Born in May, 1884, he went to the University of Kansas City Law School, married Elizabeth Wallace in 1919, and became the 33rd President of the United States. Who was he?

Harry Truman, President 1945-53

7. The first Saturday Night Live television show aired in 1975.What popular comedian was the first guest host?

George Carlin

8. What psychologist, in 1900, published a book called The Interpretation of Dreams?

Sigmund Freud

9. His entire film career lasted just more than one year in the 1950s and only three films, yet he became a widely admired screen personality, virtually synonymous with the title of one of his films. Name him and the film title.

James Dean (1931-1955) / Rebel Without a Cause

10. Name the nuclear physicist helped the Soviets develop their first hydrogen bomb, became an outspoken critic of the arms race and of Soviet repression, was exiled and was awarded the the Nobel Peace Prize.

Andrei Sakharov

Categories
Rock 'n' Roll Round 1

1. What singer of rhythm and blues was shot and killed by his father after an argument in 1984?

Marvin Gaye

2. Identify the 1990s Tom Hanks-directed film about a young, eager group called The Wonders.

That Thing You Do

3. The first rock musical opened in 1968 and became a film in 1979. What's the title?

Hair

4. Name the singers of these big hits of the 1990s:
a. Truly Madly Deeply
b. Ice Ice Baby
c. 3 AM
d. Walking on the Sun

Savage Garden
Vanilla Ice
Matchbox 20
Smash Mouth

5. Sid Vicious and Johnny Rotten were lead singers of what late 1970s British punk-rock group?

Sex Pistols

6. What is the title of the 1993 Disney film biography of Tina Turner?

What's Love Got to Do With It?

7. The lyrics of this 1965 folk-rock hit come from the Book of Ecclesiastes. Name the song title and music group.

Turn, Turn, Turn - The Byrds / "To every thing there is a season

8. What singer/songwriter, a 1950s heartthrob, wrote My Way and the theme song from The Tonight Show with Johnny Carson?

Paul Anka

9. In mid-1960s, the Beatles were the most popular group in England, the U.S., and most of the world; in Australia, however, what major group exceeded the Beatles in popularity?

Bee Gees

10. In Richmond, California, late 1970s, minister Richard Penniman warned his congregation of the evils of rock and roll music. This was very strange, since he had been one of the biggest rock and roll stars of the 1950s. Who was he?

Little Richard

Rock 'n' Roll Round 2

1. Born in the 1960s in Oakland, Stanley Burrell earned five American Music Awards, three Grammy Awards and two MTV Video Music Awards. What is the stage name of this popular rapper?

MC Hammer / also known simply as Hammer

2. Identify the group or artist of these 1980s albumns:
a. Glass Houses
b. Sports, 1984
c. Joshua Tree

Billy Joel
Huey Lewis and The News/
U2

3. What is the title of Cindy Lauper's 1984 breakthrough album that featured the song Girls Just Wanna Have Fun?

She's So Unusual

4. Name the Elton John song, a musical tribute to a blind Viet Nam veteran.

Daniel

5. This young American singer moved in 1968 to London's Notting Hill, took a demo tape to Apple Records, gained a contract, and released a debut album. Identify this singer/song writer, who was the first non-Beatle on Apple Records.

James Taylor

6. Name the artist or group for these albums:
a. Abraxas, 1970
b. Sticky Fingers, 1971

Santana
Rolling Stones

7. In its second year, 1987, what music star became the first female inducted into the Rock and Roll Hall of Fame?

Aretha Franklin, Queen of Soul

8. Big hits of the 1990s: I'll give the song title, you name the singer:
a. Baby One More Time
b. Kiss from a Rose
c. I Don't Want to Miss a Thing

Britney Spears
Seal
Aerosmith

9. Born in Texas in 1936, he was a football star, creative writer, Rhodes Scholar, singer of folk-rock and country-and-western music, and film personality. Who is he?

Kris Kristofferson

10. Who sang the theme song from Titanic?

Celine Dion

Rock 'n' Roll Round 3

1. These were summertime music hits:
a. In 1988 The Beach Boys sang about what mythical, mystical Caribbean island?
b. In 1966 The Lovin' Spoonful produced a hot and sweaty summertime smash called what?

2. In the 1990s which American musician assembled musicians who had played 50 years earlier in Havana, Cuba, and created the film the Buena Vista Social Club?

3. Name the lead singer of these groups:
a. The Wailers
b. The Four Seasons
c. Miami Sound Machine

5. Name the 1980s techno-rock band from Montreal called Men Without ... what?

6. One of the most popular British pop groups of the '80s was a duet called The Eurythmics. What two entertainers made up this group?

7. Elvis Presley's double sided hit Hound Dog / Don't Be Cruel was #1 on the Billboard charts for 11 weeks in 1956, a streak of longevity broken in 1992 by Whitney Houston's recording of what Dolly Parton song.

8. What group was composed of the singing Gibb brothers?

9. What new-wave/punk musician was a beautician, a Playboy bunny and in the 1970s lead singer of a successful rock act with what colorful group name?

10. Name the artist or group:
a. Meaty, Beaty, Big and Bouncy, 1971
b. Blondes Have More Fun, 1978
c. Stop Making Sense, 1984
d. Jagged Little Pill, 1996

Kokomo

Summer in the City

Ry Cooder

Bob Marley
Frankie Valli
Gloria Estefan

Hats

Annie Lennox / Dave Stewart

I Will Always Love You

Bee Gees

Blondie / Deborah Harry

The Who
Rod Stewart
Talking Heads / Alannis Morisette

Rock 'n' Roll Round 4

1. What 1979 song by the Sugar Hill Gang is considered the first rap music hit?

Rapper's Delight

2. Which Swedish quartet with an innocent disco sound had the number one song and album of 1994 called The Sign?

Ace of Base

3. This 1993 music album featured cover art designed by the singer's wife, a model. Name the singer, album, and artist.

Billy Joel / River of Dreams / Christie Brinkley

4. In 1986, the lead singer of the music group Talking Heads produced, directed and starred in film - a satirical look at a small town. What is his name, and the film's title?

David Byrne / True Stories

5. She was the biggest star in Tex-Mex music, but was fatally shot by one of her fans in 1995. Who was she?

Selena

6. The biggest Beatles hit written by George Harrison had a one-word title. What was it?

Something

7. In the summer of 1992, Time-Warner, Inc. became the focus of complaints because of the lyrics of a song by a controversial rap music artist in an album called Body Count. What was the name of the song, and the artist?

Cop Killer / Ice-T

8. Growing up in Liverpool, young John Lennon played with his friends in these thickly wooded gardens and later named a song after them. The gates to these gardens have become a shrine for Beatles fans from all over the world. What is the name of the garden?

Strawberry Fields

9. In January 1998, what musician became the first Hispanic artist inducted into the Rock and Roll Hall of Fame in Cleveland, Ohio?

Carlos Santana

10. What kind of foot attire did Carl Perkins and Elvis Presley sing about?

Blue suede shoes

Categories
Science Round 1

1. What point on Earth goes longest without seeing the sun, about 182 days per year?

South Pole

2. Organic chemistry is the study of compounds containing what element?

Carbon

3. In 1901 only 22% of automobiles were powered by gasoline. What were the two primary power sources at that time?

Steam 40% / Electric 38%

4. Non-identical twins, those developed from two separately fertilized ova, are called what?

Fraternal

5. The food flavoring, vanilla, is a climbing vine of what plant?

Orchid

6. The first spacecraft designed to orbit Jupiter, launched from a space shuttle in October 1989, was named for what 16th century pioneer of modern physics?

Galileo

7. What two very different objects, located in two different parts of the world, are considered the world's oldest standing structures used as observatories to study the sun, the moon, and the stars?

The Sphinx in Egypt, Stonehenge in England

8. What two long bones extend down our forearms from elbow to wrist?

Radius / Ulna

9. Two words with similar names come from the flax plant: a kind of oil, and a kind of fiber. What are they?

Linseed / Linen

10. Which planet was first photographed at the Lowell Observatory in Flagstaff, Arizona in 1930?

Pluto

Science Round 2

1. According to physics, what are the three basic phases of physical matter?

Solid, Liquid, Gas

2. What is meant by the perigee of a planet or moon?

The point in its orbit in which the body is closest to the Earth

3. What chemical gas, NH3, was named for the temple of Amen, in Libya, where it was first obtained?

Ammonia

4. Name these common electric units:
a. Electric current
b. Electric power
c. Electric potential

Ampere
Watt
Volt

5. Ancient civilizations believed that this element filled the space beyond the earth's atmosphere. In 1846, doctors first used it as an anaesthetic. What is it?

Ether

6. What number is associated with circadian rhythm?

24 hours, the Biological Clock

7. A triple-A (AAA) battery measures how many volts?

1 volt

8. Which scientist in the early 1900's discovered the chemical element called radium?

Marie Curie, originally Manja Skoodowska, Polish-Born French chemist (1867-1934)

9. In spite of his severe handicap, he is considered the greatest theoretical physicist of the late 20th century. Who is he, and what chronic disease does he have?

Stephen Hawking / Amyotrophic Lateral Sclerosis (ALS), also called Lou Gehrig's disease

10. Which adult beverage, made from the agave plant, is named after a town of west-central Mexico?

Tequila

Science Round 3

1. Besides Earth, all the other planets in our solar system are named after what?

Mythological figures

2. If someone suffers from myopia, what can they not do well?

See distances clearly

3. Sea water is, on average, what percent salt?

3-4% range

4. Scientists and archeologists can estimate the age of an ancient object by measuring its remains of what radioactive carbon isotope?

Carbon 14, with atomic mass 14 and half-life 5,780 years

5. Those marine crustaceans that attach themselves to bottoms of ships are called what?

Barnacles

6. The average adult body contains about how many quarts of blood?

Five

7. What is the most dense planet in our solar system?

Earth

8. This chemical element, with atomic number 22, is a strong, light-weight metallic element used in aircraft metals and golf clubs, and is named for giants of Greek mythology. What element?

Titanium

9. Absolute zero registers at how many degrees Celsius?

-273° C

10. This chemical element, atomic #53, was extracted from brine and seaweed around 1811, and has always been known as a disinfectant. What is it?

Iodine

Science Round 4

1. First developed in 1990, what became part of the Internet in 1991?

The World Wide Web

2. In chemistry: In a litmus test, what color does the test strip turn after coming in contact with each of the following?
a. An acid
b. A base

Turns red
Turns blue

3. What Italian astronomer and physicist was the first person to use a telescope to study the stars, around 1610?

Galileo Galilei (1564-1642)

4. Regarding clouds:
a. What do we call those large, white puffy clouds that are usually a sign of good weather?
b. What do we call the dark clouds characteristic of storms?
c. What do we call the lacy or wispy clouds that generally precede a change in the weather?

Cumulus

Nimbus

Cirrus

5. After the diamond, this is the hardest gemstone. It naturally occurs in blue, purple, green, white, pink, gold, and orange. Which gemstone?

Sapphire

6. What animal creates pearls, and why?

Oysters - to alleviate an irritation, like a grain of sand, the oyster covers it with a spherical layer of nacre, or mother-of-pearl

7. What do we call a pair of colors whose mixture produces white light?

Complementary colors

8. The scale that measures the percentage of water in the atmosphere is known by what two-word phrase?

Relative humidity

9. What do we call the type of light wave that is shorter than radio waves but longer than infrared waves?

Microwaves

10. In the 1920s, before his discovery of penicillin, Alexander Fleming discovered an antiseptic bacteria fighter called lysozime, an enzyme that appears naturally in the human body. What do we more commonly call lysozime?

Saliva / Tears

Categories
Sports Round 1

1. On November 13, 2000, the Michigan State men's basketball team defeated what team, ending their 1,270 game winning streak?

Harlem Globetrotters

2. How many players are there on a polo team: 4, 6, or 8?

4

3. Name four Olympic sports in which opponents are on opposite sides of a net?

Tennis / Volleyball / Ping Pong / Badminton

4. What explosive sporting event lasts about 1/2000th of a second and generates 10,000 pounds of force?

Bat hitting baseball (not as much power explodes with a hockey puck)

5. Of the five sports that made up the ancient olympic pentathlon, three of them were running, jumping, and wrestling. What were the other two?

Discus Throw / Javelin or Spear Throw

6. Which one of these basketball stars was NOT the number one pick in the NBA draft: Shaquille O'Neal, Michael Jordan, Magic Johnson?

Michael Jordan

7. What world-class female tennis star won at least one of the major Grand Slam tournaments for 13 consecutive years, from 1974-86?

Chris Evert

8. In 1977, future superstar football quarterback Joe Montana led what college team to the national championship?

Notre Dame

9. In which sport has the oldest winner been 18 years old, and the youngest about 2-3 years old?

Horse racing

10. What two events make up the Winter Olympic event called the biathlon?

Cross-country skiing and rifle shooting

Sports Round 2

1. What two major league baseball players in 2001 hit a record 137 homers - the most of any two players in a season?

Barry Bonds (73) and Sammy Sosa (64)

2. This crippled 11-year old girl just wanted to run and play like her other friends. By the time she was 20, in 1960, she had won Olympic gold medals in track and field for the United States. Who was she?

Wilma Rudolph

3. Identify these National Basketball Association team names and cities:
a. Named for an annoying insect
b. Named for a car part
c. Named for an art form

Charlotte Hornets
Detroit Pistons
Utah Jazz

4a. What is the golf term for one shot under par?
b. What about two shots under par?

Birdie
Eagle

5. What country outside of Europe or South America has been succesful in World-Cup soccer games? (1930-present)

Mexico

6. In 1984 this person became the all-time leading scorer in National Basketball Association history. Who was it?

Kareem Abdul-Jabbar

7. Identify a major league baseball team named after each of the following:
a. Beer makers
b. Police
c. Religious leaders

Milwaukee Brewers
Texas Rangers
San Diego Padres

8. In 1998, her career income from tennis exceeded $20 million, making her the all time #1 money-earning female athlete up to that time. Who is she?

Steffi Graf

9. The world championships for this Asian sport were first held in 1970 in Tokyo, and women first competed in 1980. What sport?

Karate

10. The modern rules of what sport were formulated in 1867 by British aristocrat the Marquis of Queensbury?

Boxing

Sports Round 3

1. Which tennis player won the Wimbledon men's singles title every year from 1976 through 1980?

2. Which professional basketball team won almost 9,000 consecutive games between 1971 and 1995?

3. What major league baseball teams won the World Series most frequently in each of these decades:
a. 1990s?
b. 1970s?
c. 1950s?

4. In a baseball field, is the pitcher's mound located closer to 2nd base, closer to home plate, or exactly halfway between?

5. In April, 1997, 21-year-old golf prodigy Tiger Woods became the first black golfer to win what prestigious golf tournament, held each year in what Georgia city?

6. Name the college football bowl games named after each of the following:
a. ... a Spanish festival
b. ... an animal
c. ... a greeting

7. One of the great comebacks of the 1990's belongs to a tennis star who returned to the sport two years after being stabbed by a tennis fan. Who is she?

8. Fill in the missing word in this quotation: Football quarterback Joe Namath said, "When you win, _____ hurts."

9. What two National Football League teams are located in cities named after bodies of water?

10. Major League Baseball spring training leagues, held in Florida and Arizona, are known by what two names?

Bjorn Borg

Harlem Globetrotters

Atlanta Braves (4)
Cincinnati Reds (4)
New York Yankees (8) times

Closer to home

Masters /
Augusta, Georgia

Fiesta Bowl
Gator Bowl
Aloha Bowl

Monica Seles

Nothing!

Green Bay, Wisconsin /
Tampa Bay, Florida

Cactus League /
Grapefruit League

Sports Round 4

1. Name three major league baseball teams whose city name and team name begin with the same letter of the alphabet.

Chicago Cubs / Philadelphia Phillies / Pittsburgh Pirates

2. On March 2, 1962, the all time record for points scored in a single NBA basketball game was set, when what great athlete scored how many points?

Wilt Chamberlain / 100 points

3. Most sports fans agree that the Irish, French, English, and Kentucky are the four greatest what?

Horse racing derbies

4. The world's first international soccer football game took place in 1872, between teams from what two lands?

England and Scotland

5. In many sports, the units of play are called halves, quarters, etc. What are they called in each of the following sports?
a. Baseball
b. Ice Hockey
c. Bowling
d. Polo

Innings
Periods
Frames
Chukkers

6. From 1968 to 1980, four consecutive Summer Olympic Games were held in cities beginning with the letter M. Name these cities.

Mexico City / Munich / Montreal / Moscow

7. Olympic History:
a. In what year were the first ancient Olympic Games played?
b. At what location in Greece?

776 B.C.

Olympia, on the Peloponnesian Peninsula

8. Give the nicknames of these college football teams:
a. Notre Dame
b. University of Florida
c. University of Texas

Fighting Irish
Gators
Longhorns

9. On October 2, 1920, the Cincinnati Reds and the Pittsburgh Pirates did something on the same day, that no baseball teams have ever done since. What did they do?

Played a triple-header, three games in one day

10. Boxer Muhammad Ali was born with what name?

Cassius Clay

Master Quiz

(Challenges for Experts)

Master Quiz (Challenges for Experts)
Master Round 1

1. The 1993 Nobel Peace Prize was shared by two African leaders, former political adversaries. Name them?

Nelson Mandela / Frederik De Klerk

2. In 1998, the American Film Institute announced its list of the 100 Best Films of all time. Which film topped their list?

Citizen Kane, 1941

3. What 12th century Archbishop of Canterbury, killed by the king's men, is featured in plays by T.S. Eliot (Murder in the Cathedral) and the French playwright Jean Anouilh?

Thomas à Becket, people from all over the world visit his burial place

4. What complex molecule carries oxygen in the blood and gives blood its characteristic red color?

Hemoglobin

5. Supply the Latin translation for:
a. To infinity
b. In good faith
c. Seize the day

Ad Infinitum
Bona Fide
Carpe Diem

6. What is the 6-letter name of the single cell that results from the union of the parents' sex cells at fertilization?

Zygote

7. Which U.S. city has about 20 colleges and universities, including the first art school in the United States (1805), the oldest art school for women (1844), and the first medical school exclusively for women (1850)?

Philadelphia

8. In April, 1990, former enemies signed a cease-fire agreement ending an eight-year civil war in which North American country?

Nicaragua

9. The Capitolio Nationale in Havana, Cuba, the capital building constructed in 1929, is an almost exact replica of the capital building in what other city?

Washington, D.C.

10. In the 1840s, Henry Wells (of Wells Fargo bank) established a company to transport people and their valuables. This company is still well known today in the business of money and travel. What is it?

American Express

Master Round 2

1. According to the Guiness Book of Records, the most money ever paid to a film actor was the $50-$60 million that Jack Nicholson earned playing which unusual character in which 1989 Tim Burton film?

The Joker / Batman

2. This 13th century Italian monk and theologian, who sought to reconcile faith and Aristotelian logic, was named a saint of the Roman Catholic Church. Who is he?

Saint Thomas Aquinas

3. Which 320-island nation of the southwest Pacific Ocean was discovered in 1643 by Dutch navigator Abel Tasman, annexed by Great Britain in 1874, and became independent in 1970?

Fiji, with capital Suva

4. Possibly the largest Islamic mosque outside of Saudi Arabia is this giant structure built along the Atlantic Ocean in what African city?

Casablanca, Morocco

5. What fastest selling single record of all time sold 32 million copies in 37 days of 1997. What was the title, and which British superstar recorded it?

Candle in the Wind / Elton John (on death of Diana)

6. The oldest continuously inhabited settlement in the Western Hemisphere was established in 1496 by Bartholomew Columbus (Christopher's brother), and today it is capital of its country. What city is it?

Santo Domingo, Dominican Republic

7. If the length, width, and height of a rectangular box all increase by 50%, then the volume increases by what percentage?

237.5% If old volume was "1" then the new volume is 3.375

8. In 1998, Australian Susie Maroney set a world record when she did this for 38 hours and 33 minutes. What did she do, and where did she do it?

Swam - longest nonstop ocean swim by a woman, from Mexico to Cuba

9. What large country, in 1920, was the world's first to legalize abortion?

Soviet Union

10. In 1507 German mapmaker Martin Martinseemuller was the first to apply what name on a map of the new world?

America - He thought Amerigo Vespucci discovered the New World.

Master Round 3

1. To the relief of millions of his subjects, which brutal world leader died on March 5, 1953?

Joseph Stalin

2. Madame Tussaud's waxworks in London has cloned politicians, film stars and pop idols, including two music groups. One was The Beatles in 1964. Who is the other?

Spice Girls, in 1999

3. What resort city of south-central Germany, lying in the foothills of the Alps near Oberammergau, was the site of the 1936 Winter Olympics?

Garmisch-Partenkirchen

4. Which three countries hosted the Winter Olympics during the decade of the 1990s?

Nagano, Japan, 1998 / Liljehammer Norway 1994 / Albertville, France 1992

5. This Italian military and political leader of the late 15th century, along with his sister, was known for treachery and cruelty. In fact, he was the model for Machiavelli's The Prince. Can you identify him and his sister?

Cesare and Lucrezia Borgia

6. This region northeast of Turkey with a 2500-year old history was first to adopt Christianity as a national religion. Today it's an independent country with what name?

Armenia

7. What early settlers of England sound like they came from a geometry book?

Angles, Germanic tribes together with the Jutes and Saxons formed the Anglo-Saxon peoples.

8. Which Nigerian writer wrote the 1958 novel Things Fall Apart, describing traditional African life in conflict with colonial rule and westernization.

Chinua Achebe

9. In an attempt to control their own work, what film studio did Charlie Chaplin, D.W. Griffith, Douglas Fairbanks, and Mary Pickford establish in 1919?

United Artists

10. What are the two most populous capital cities in the U.S.A.? (data 2001)

Phoenix, Arizona / Indianapolis, Indiana

Master Round 4

1. What empire lost its domination of central Europe as a result of World War I?

Austro-Hungarian

2. In the second millennium B.C., this Phoenician city north of present day Beirut was the most important city in the eastern Mediterranean. Alphabetic writing was first practiced there and books of papyrus were made there. In fact the name of an extremely well-known book comes from the name of this city. What is it?

Byblos

3. One of the last words in the dictionary is zymology, a science related to a type of beverage. What is it?

Fermentation / Brewing

4. Which 20th century British scholar coined the phrase, "Work expands to fill the time available for its completion"?

Northcote Parkinson / Parkinson's Law

5. According to Greek and Roman mythology, these hideous, winged goddesses relentlessly pursued evildoers. Today their name is synonymous with violent, uncontrolled action. Who were they?

Furies

6. Name the ruling dynasty (or house) of the following British monarchs:
a. Henry II
b. Henry V
c. Henry VIII

Plantagenet
Lancaster
Tudor

7. Of the Academy Award winning best pictures from 1949 and 1950, both begin with the word All. Name these film titles?

All the King's Men / All About Eve

8. If a rocket could fly from the Earth to the sun at a speed of 1,000 km. per hour, about how many years would the trip take? Closer to 8, 17, or 25?

17.2 years
Time = Distance divided by Rate ---> (150 Million km) ÷ (8.77 million km/Year)

9. This magnificent domed cathedral in Istanbul, Turkey, was once the central church building of the Eastern Orthodox Church, and is now a museum. Name it.

Hagia Sophia (or Santa Sophia or Saint Sophia or Agia Sophia)

10. The city/state of Carthage, founded 9th century B.C. by the Phoenicians, was home of Hannibal, whose forces crossed the Alps and routed Roman armies, 200 B.C. In which modern country is Carthage located?

Tunisia

Master Round 5

1. What does the adjective hircine (hûr-shin) mean: hairy, well-dressed, or smelling like a goat?

Acting or smelling like a goat, from hircus - goat

2. The 15th century paintings of this Flemish artist are filled with tiny bizarre details of people, plants and animals. One of his most famous paintings is The Garden of Earthly Delights. Who is this forerunner of surrealism?

Hieronymous Bosch

3. These are nautical measurements:
a. What unit of measurement is equal to one nautical mile per hour?

Knot

b. What unit of nautical distance is equal to 3 miles (4.8 km.)?

League

c. What unit of nautical distance is equal to 6 feet (1.8 km.)?

Fathom

4. What is the top money making film series of them all - over $4 billion has been grossed from at least 18 films with the same theme or character?

James Bond

5. The first televised news coverage of soldiers invading a foreign country occurred in what war?

Korean War, 1950

6. In which country is each of these languages primarily spoken?
a. Castilian
b. Amharic
c. Urdu

Spain
Ethopia
Pakistan

7. With over 90 million inhabitants, what island of Japan is the world's most highly populated island?

Honshu - Tokyo is located there

8. During which 14th-15th century war did Joan of Arc rally the French against English invaders?

100 Years War

9. What nickname for a scolding, nagging woman is named for a small mouse-like animal?

Shrew

10. What is known in Tibetan as Goddess Mother of the World?

Mt. Everest / Chomolungma

Master Round 6

1. In 1959, what isolated state became the first U.S. state to require that married women take their husbands' last names?

Hawaii

2. Ancient Japan was divided into four discrete social classes: fourth was traders, third was artisans, second was farmers. What was the highest class?

Samurai or Warriors

3. What product does a sommelier deal with?

Wine - a sommelier is a wine steward in a restaurant

4. The author Henry David Thoreau was jailed for refusing to pay a tax to support what 1846-48 war? What was the title of the essay he wrote explaining the principles of his action?

Mexican War / Civil disobedience

5. Beginning in 1927, can you name any of the first four women to win the Academy Award as Best Actress?

1927 Janet Gaynor; 1928 Mary Pickford; 1929 Norma Shearer; 1930 Marie Dressler

6. What two-word phrase with a number in it can be defined in two ways: a state of great joy and satisfaction, or the Moslem dwelling place of God and the angels.

Seventh Heaven

7. In 1965, Rhodesia declared independence from Britain:
a. Who was the Rhodesian leader at that time?
b. Rhodesia's name was later changed to what?
c. Name the former and current capital city.

Ian Smith
Zimbabwe
Salisbury / Harare

8. Who is the Roman goddess of wisdom, invention, and the arts?

Minerva

9. Henry VIII's 1533 divorce from what woman caused his break with Roman Catholicism and the beginning of the Church of English?

Catherine of Aragon

10. Which recording group and what performer sold the most single records in each of these countries during the 1970s?
a. In the United States

Elton John / The Bee Gees

b. In the United Kingdom

Abba / Rod Stewart

Master Round 7

1. Which French physician and astrologer wrote a 1555 book of prophecies called Centuries?

Nostradamus, originally Michel de Notredame (1503-1566)

2. Who was ruler of Egypt when the Great Pyramid at Giza was built?

Cheops, originally Khufu (2590-2567 B.C.)

3. Give the last names of these well-known composers of classical music whose last names all begin with B:
a. Leonard
b. Johannes
c. Bela

Bernstein
Brahms
Bartok

4. One of the earliest popular radio comedies starred Freeman Gosden and Charles J. Correll, and featured characters named Kingfish and Lightnin'. What was this radio show?

Amos 'n' Andy

5. Which two British actors share the dubious record of being nominated for an Academy Award seven times, but never victorious?

Richard Burton / Peter O'Toole

6. These organizations of artisans in the Middle Ages were formed to control the quality and price of products. What do we call these predecessors of trade unions?

Guilds

7. Which poet wrote this line, and what's the next line: "East is East, and West is West, ..."

Rudyard Kipling / "... and never the twain shall meet"

8. The environmental protection movement was energized in 1962 with the publication of what book by Rachel Carson?

Silent Spring

9. Which kind of tank is the Brookings Institute, and in which city is it located?

Think Tank/ Washington, D.C.

10. Identify three types of clothing fabric named after places in India.

Madras / Cashmere (Kashmir) / Calico (Calcutta)

Master Round 8

1. Spanish explorer Vasco Nunez de Balboa discovered the Pacific Ocean September 13, 1513, at which location along the Pacific?

Panama. He crossed the Isthmus of Panama by land from the Atlantic and Gulf of Mexico

2. Which branch of philosophy deals with the nature and expression of beauty?

Aesthetics

3. Intended for the welfare of its subjects, what was created by the British Parliament in 1689 and the U.S. Congress in 1791?

A Bill of Rights - a declaration of rights of citizens

4. By what percent must you lengthen each side of a square in order to double its area?

41% - if each side grows from 1 unit of length to 1.41, then the area (length times width) will grow from 1 square unit to 2 square units

5. Which British inventor invented the air-filled rubber tire around 1887?

John Dunlop, (1840-1921)

6. Justinian the Great was a 5-6th century leader of which empire?

Byzantine

7. The mother of what Shakespearean character says, "The lady doth protest too much"?

Hamlet- after an actress in a play swears never to remarry if her husband dies

8. Name two films directed by Frank Capra that begin with the word Mr.:
a. 1939 film starring James Stewart

b. 1936 film starring Gary Cooper

Mr. Smith Goes to Washington / Mr. Deeds Goes to Town

9. Words ending with the letters ...oid:
a. Stay clear of...
b. Small celestial bodies lying chiefly between Mars and Jupiter that revolve around the Sun...
c. Nicotine, cocaine, and morphine, among others...

Avoid
Meteoroid

Alkaloid

10. What country has the largest number of universities, twice as many as the U.S.A.?

India

Master Round 9

1. Chemically, what medical product is known as hydrated magnesium sulfate, and is named after the horse-racing town in England where it was originally produced?

Epsom Salts, originally produced at mineral springs not far from Epsom

2. What three Caribbean islands that begin with A, B, and C, lie in the Netherlands Antilles (Dutch West Indies)?

Aruba / Bonaire / Curacao

3. In 1925 in Tennessee a teacher went on trial for teaching Charles Darwin's theory of evolution. Who was he, what lawyer defended him, and which famous lawyer was on the prosecution side?

John Scopes / Clarence Darrow / William Jennings Bryan

4. What 20th century Russian-born pianist, noted for his interpretations of Chopin and Liszt, who has been called the crown prince of romantic piano?

Vladimir Horowitz (1904-1989)

5. Name the artists:
a. 14th century Italian who painted the Birth of Venus
b. 19th century French impressionist who created The Boating Party

Boticelli
Renoir

6. In which year ending with 9 did these things happen?
a. The word Apartheid was first used, and Kodak introduced a 16 mm color movie film
b. Napoleon Bonaparte was born

1929

1769

7. What 19th century Danish philosopher, who wrote about fear, loneliness, and religion, is considered a forerunner of existential philosophy?

Soren Kierkegaard

8. Born in India in 1936, Arnold Dorsey became a British singer and actor, taking his stage name from that of a German composer. Name this popular singer.

Engelbert Humperdinck

9. In the 13-17th century some free towns in northern Germany and neighboring areas joined what confederation for economic and defensive reasons.

Hanseatic League

10. Which popular magazine is named for the 19th century William Thackeray novel, featuring the unscrupulous Becky Sharp, who gains wealth and influence by her cleverness.

Vanity Fair

Master Round 10

1. Four, raised to what power, is eight?

2. This mountain range connecting Pakistan and Afghanistan has been used as invasion and trade routes since ancient times. It's named after a religion. What is it?

3. Which Venezuelan revolutionary leader liberated the northern part of South America from the grip of the Spanish in 1819?

4. It's possible to have more than $1.00 in coins, yet not be able to make exact change for one dollar. What is the largest amount of money you could have, in coins, and not be able to make exact change for one dollar?

5. Which Polish scholar, in 1543, provided the foundation for modern astronomy when he produced a model of the solar system with the sun at the center?

6. Can you name the two best-known works of Russian author Leo Tolstoy?

7. At the first Academy Award ceremony in 1928, the Academy Board declared what progressive film ineligible for the best film award due to unfair comparison with all other films, but gave an honorary award instead?

8a. What sixteenth century religious movement resulted in the founding of the Protestant Church?
b. When this movement was established in England in 1534, what king declared himself head of the Christian Church in England?

9. What three-letter Latin abbreviation is sometimes written at the end of mathematical or scientific proofs, and what does it mean?

10. The United States and Russia are separated by what narrow stretch of water?

1.5

Hindu Kush

Simon Bolivar

$1.19 = 3 quarters, 4 dimes, 4 pennies

Nicolaus Copernicus

War and Peace / Anna Karenina

The Jazz Singer

The Reformation

Henry VIII

QED, Quod Erat Demonstrandum - to be demonstrated.

Bering Strait - between Alaska and Siberia

Trivia Party - Team Answer Sheet

Team Number _____ Round Number _____

1.

2.

3.

4.

5.

6.

7.

8.

9.

10.

Trivia Party - Master Score Sheet

TEAM	ROUND 1	ROUND 2	ROUND 3	ROUND 4	ROUND 5	TOTAL
	This round / Current score	This round / Current score	This round / Current score	This round / Current score	This round / Current score	
	This round / Current score	This round / Current score	This round / Current score	This round / Current score	This round / Current score	
	This round / Current score	This round / Current score	This round / Current score	This round / Current score	This round / Current score	
	This round / Current score	This round / Current score	This round / Current score	This round / Current score	This round / Current score	
	This round / Current score	This round / Current score	This round / Current score	This round / Current score	This round / Current score	
	This round / Current score	This round / Current score	This round / Current score	This round / Current score	This round / Current score	

You may order
Trivia Café: 2000 Questions for Parties, Fund-raisers, School Events & Travel
by Howard Rachelson
ISBN 1-56550-090-3
from your local bookstore, Amazon.com
or
directly from the publisher

To order copies directly from VBI by mail use this order form:

Number of books: _____ at $16.00 per book $_____

Sales tax of 7.25% applies to books mailed to California addresses only:

Number of books: _____ at $1.16 per copy $_____

Shipping and handling at $3.50 for first book (add $2 for each additional book)

                                        _____books $_____

                        Total amount enclosed $_____

Name:_____

Mailing address:_____

City:_____State:_____Zip_____

Please send a check or money order (no cash or C.O.D.) to:
Vision Books International
775 East Blithedale Ave. #342
Mill Valley, CA 94941

Visit our Web site at www.vbipublishing.com